# Thinking in Chinese:

## An American's Journey into the Chinese Mind

# Thinking in Chinese:

## An American's Journey into the Chinese Mind

Jeffrey G. Brown, M.D.

Artwork by Linda Wang

This book is a work of fiction. Places, events, and situations in this story are completely fictional. Any resemblance to actual persons, living or dead, is purely coincidental.

ISBN: 0-9725884-0-X

*To my parents,*

*For supporting me all the way*

# Table of Contents

# Introduction

Chinese civilization is 5,000 years old. It is the longest-standing, continuous civilization in the history of the world. When the pharaohs were constructing pyramids in Egypt, the Chinese were building magnificent temples. When Plato was writing his *Discourses on the Republic*, the Chinese were debating the ethics of man. The pyramids are still standing, and the *Republic* is still vibrant, but the civilizations that produced them have long since passed. The Chinese, on the other hand, remain. China has been invaded multiple times. It has suffered poverty, famine and natural disasters. Yet the foundations of this ancient culture are still firm and intact. Despite what seem insurmountable circumstances, China re-groups, re-arranges and overcomes.

Running through Chinese culture, from ancient times to the present, is perhaps the most enigmatic and fascinating creation of the Chinese mind: the Chinese character. The Chinese character, the written form of spoken Chinese, is the glue that binds together the Chinese culture.[1] Shi Huang Di, the first emperor of Imperial China, recognized this fact in 221 BC, when in his desire to unify a fragmented nation set as his first order of business standardization of the characters.

The Chinese character possesses qualities completely unlike those found in Western languages. Whereas English has 26 letters and innumerable words, Chinese has 50,000 Chinese characters. Each character has its own unique script and needs to be learned as a separate entity. Characters are pronounced with a single monosyllable, which can have one of several tonal variations. And whereas the spelling of English words approximates their sound, in Chinese, the character and its sound seem only remotely related. The character can be pronounced in several different ways, depending on the particular spoken dialect. In fact, the various Chinese dialects are mutually unintelligible. Across dialects, people can only communicate through use of the characters.

When I first visited China in 1991, I had very little knowledge of the Chinese language. Throughout college, I had focused my efforts on my pre-medical course-work: physics, chemistry and biology. I graduated from college and was accepted to medical school. But ever since I could remember, I had an intense curiosity regarding the Chinese culture. The first step, I decided, was to study Chinese. Postponing my acceptance to medical school, I applied for a visa, flew to Beijing and went to work studying the Chinese language.

As a Westerner living in China with only a basic knowledge of the language and culture, it is easy to assume that Chinese culture is becoming more like the West. Although the standard of living was still quite low, and job opportunities still limited, the country was developing rapidly in every dimension. It seemed that everyone I met wanted to practice his English or study in an American university. People wore Western-style clothes, drank Coca-Cola and craved all aspects of American popular culture.

The tendency in the West is to ignore differences among cultures and assume that all people think in more or less the same way. We are clearly proud of our culture, and we like to think that other cultures share our love of individuality and self-reliance. Our scientific research sets the international standard, and science is considered the most objective and fair representation of facts. Western academics tend to be dismissive of foreign scholarship unless it approaches the "scientific method." We apply our scientific thinking not only to medicine and physics, but to "social science," "political science" and linguistics as well.

Yet as similar as these two cultures appeared on the surface, there was something uncannily different. Take, for example, the idea of "individuality," perhaps the fundamental concept of modern American culture. "Individuality" is the idea that every person is different and unique. From childhood on, we are taught to be "creative," "original" and to pursue our individual "dreams." "Conformity" in American culture has a negative connotation. It suggests blind acceptance to old, established ways. Our political life is fundamentally based on the individual: individual freedoms and individual rights.

What do we mean when we say an individual has rights? We mean that regardless of any other considerations, whether or not something is good for the group as a whole, the individual takes precedence. Say, for example, a company injures an individual. The individual sues the company and is awarded $50 million. Some may say that the settlement was high, but most can agree that justice was served. Subsequently, the company goes out of business and 30 people are put out of work. By protecting the rights of one individual we have to a lesser degree injured 30 others.

Chinese culture doesn't value "individuality." Chinese culture values the group. In America, we sacrifice the group for the good of the individual. In China, they sacrifice the individual for the good of the group. Traditionally, there is no concept of "rights" in Chinese culture. Rather, there are responsibilities. Children are not taught to develop their own interests. They are taught to conform to specific roles and established patterns. People are not defined by their differences. They are defined by their place in the group.

There is no right or wrong approach here. Rather, there are two distinctly different ways of thinking. But why should there be such a difference? Although it seems like an impossible question, there is actually a simple answer: it is because of the languages. Americans think in English. Chinese think in Chinese. Something about the two languages makes these cultures think in entirely different ways.

The Chinese character and the Chinese language are the key to understanding the Chinese culture. As we will see, the organization of the Chinese characters is what guides the organization of the other entities as well: cooking, medicine, history and society. The manner in which the Chinese think about medicine, for example, is the same manner in which they think about history and cooking. Chinese culture is a cohesive unit, and each of these topics is intimately connected. During the course of this book, as I travel abroad, study Chinese and visit with various individuals, I learn that Western "science" is only one way of thinking, and that it has its roots in Western languages. The unique organization of the Chinese language forms the psychological basis for thinking in Chinese.

## -- 1 --
## Language and Thought

"I don't know the connection between language and thought," said the old man as we gripped the seat in front of us and held on for dear life. The rusted old bus twisted and turned its way around the bend, just missing a car coming from the other direction. In the distance lay the city, its multitude of people, its harried way of life, all now comfortably resting under a giant cloud of gray dust.

It wasn't really fair, this question about language and thought. It was so vague and philosophical, so abstract and unclear--certainly not a topic for casual conversation. It was more reminiscent of a college sophomore essay than a question to a stranger on a bus. Nonetheless, the man was so old and wrinkled. I figured he must somehow know the answer.

"It's like the story of Zhuang Zhou and the butterfly," he said finally.

9

"Zhuang-who?" I said curiously, perking up my ears. The bus took another sharp turn. Bits of debris sprayed against the window, obscuring the view of the cliff below.

"Zhuang Zhou was a philosopher from the Zhou Dynasty," he said politely, looking out through bottomless brown eyes. "One night he fell asleep and dreamed he was a butterfly. There he was, a little butterfly flying to and fro, completely unaware that he was Zhuang Zhou."

"What happened?"

"Zhuang Zhou awoke. He touched his body and confirmed that he was indeed Zhuang Zhou. But," cautioned the old man, "he didn't know if it was Zhuang Zhou who dreamed he was a butterfly, or if he was now a butterfly dreaming he was Zhuang Zhou."

I failed to see his point.

"Language influences our thoughts. But thoughts also influence our language. It's a combination of both."

"A combination?"

This question of the relationship between language and thought was something of an anomaly. It had consumed my thoughts ever since I set foot in this ancient and mysterious country. Chinese and Western cultures were different in such a multitude of ways--not only the

10

physical appearance of the people--but also the food, the philosophy and the social interactions. It was as if the history of the world had made a sudden left turn and flung each culture its separate way.

Chinese culture is a combination of elements: a revered and ritualized imperial past, some 20th century political philosophy, then a magnificent stride toward modernization. Yet even with its Western dress and its automobiles, its shopping malls and its fast-food chains, everything is similar--but nothing is entirely the same. Beneath a familiar Western façade roams an entirely different animal.

Not only are the cultures different, but the languages are different as well. Whereas the letters of the English alphabet represent the sounds of spoken speech, Chinese characters seem to represent the meaning directly. Some characters are like pictures, such as a man or a bird. Others are completely abstract. Each character is a unique arrangement of lines and curves, and each has its own separate meaning.

People use language to construct ideas. It is difficult to imagine a "thought" without the words used to describe it. Americans think in English. Chinese think in Chinese. Perhaps, I thought to myself, the Chinese language, in some unrecognized way, had influenced the development of Chinese thought.

Despite the fact that it contradicts almost every notion of modern linguistics, the idea that language might influence thought is not completely original. Many authors have attempted to show a connection. In the 1860's, the German philosopher Adolph Trendelenburg (1802-1872) suggested that if Aristotle had spoken Chinese, the categories of Aristotelian logic would have been entirely different.[2]

Ezra Pound, the famous American poet, felt that Chinese characters, with their breadth of meaning and overall ambiguity, made Chinese naturally suited for writing poetry.[3]

Other authors suggested that the Chinese characters, because of their pictographic representation of ideas or objects, made Chinese thinking more "concrete."[4]

Linguist Alfred Bloom wrote that because Chinese lacks certain grammatical constructions (counterfactuals), it cannot express certain thoughts.[5]

And, finally, numerous authors have attempted to link the Chinese language to the early lack of "science" in Chinese culture.[6] Despite China's early invention of paper, printing and gunpowder, science did not systematically progress as it did in the West.

Of course, most modern linguists agree that because of differences in vocabulary and grammar, some thoughts are more easily expressed or "codified" in some languages than others. For example, an individual whose language makes a distinction between "orange" and "yellow" may have less difficulty in describing the two colors than an individual whose language has a single word for both.

However, few modern linguists embrace the idea that language significantly influences thought. Rather, the bulk of modern linguistics is based on the premise that, despite considerable differences among the various world languages, there is a single set of "mental rules" that underlies them all. These mental rules, termed the "Universal Grammar," are present at birth and are part of the genetically inherited structure of the human brain. The rules provide the basis for our thoughts. Our thoughts are independent of our particular spoken language.

Linguist Steven Pinker explains,

> There is no scientific evidence that languages dramatically shape their speakers' way of thinking.

He continues,

> Knowing about the ubiquity of complex language across individuals and cultures and the single mental design underlying them all, no speech seems foreign to me, even when I cannot understand a word. The banter among New

Guinean highlanders in the film of their first contact with the rest of the world, the motions of a sign language interpreter, the prattle of little girls in a Tokyo playground--I imagine seeing through the rhythms to the structures underneath, and sense that we all have the same minds.[7]

I looked out over the vast stretch of mountains and valleys. The concept of a Universal Grammar certainly seemed plausible. Some mental design, part of the inherent structure of the human brain, could conceivably allow humans to learn and utilize language. But it wasn't the whole story. From China to the West, from one culture to the next, the most common assumptions of everyday life had suddenly and unequivocally changed. I wasn't sure why and I couldn't explain how, but I had the slowly creeping, sinking suspicion that it had something to do with the language.

Of course, the problem of demonstrating that language influences thought is the problem of finding a good example. In order to claim that language influences perception of time, for example, one needs to describe a person's perception of time, and why it is necessarily different from the speaker of a different language. Describing an abstract notion such as "time" is difficult, however, without relying on terms for "time" that are found in that language. In the absence of a non-linguistic way of defining "perception of time," the results are circular and less than convincing.

The bus climbed steadily up the dirt road, nearing the site of the famous monastery where we would sit and sip their famous tea. The old man had fallen deep into thought and I, likewise, the same. And perhaps in a different life, if I was somewhat more cynical or slightly less interested, I would have dismissed these notions of language and thought as nothing more than a fantasy. I would have entered medical school, as I had originally intended, and lost in the details of some patient's chart, it would all seem a distant memory---a memory, that is, were it not for one peculiar, inexplicable conundrum: Chinese medicine.

Chinese medicine, the ancient art of Chinese healing, was ostensibly the original reason why I came to China. It was back in the U.S. during my last months of college, when I noticed a bulletin offering a language scholarship for China. One individual would be offered the rare opportunity to spend a year in China studying Chinese.

I had always been interested in Chinese culture, ever since those Friday nights as a child when my parents would order Chinese takeout. I immediately prepared the application essay. As I was already accepted to a U.S. medical school, the purpose of my application was clear. I was going to study Chinese medicine.

At the time, I didn't know much about Chinese medicine, so one cold Midwestern night, I made the long lonely trek to the library to see what I could find. There, hidden deep within the stacks, I opened a half-dozen books on Chinese medicine and began to read.

I soon discovered that Chinese medicine is 5,000 years old, beginning with the legendary emperor Shen Nong. Since that time, Chinese medicine has developed a wide range of diagnostic and therapeutic modalities, completely unlike those found in Western medicine. Whereas Western physicians increasingly rely on x-ray studies and laboratory tests, Chinese physicians place their emphasis on the appearance of the tongue and the quality of the pulse. There are no operations or invasive procedures in Chinese medicine. Physicians strive to alter *Qi* (pronounced "tchee"), the body's natural essence, by the use of exercise, herbs and acupuncture.

Furthermore, whereas Western medicine is founded on the scientific principles of physics, chemistry and biology, Chinese medicine is founded on the philosophic principles of Yin-Yang and Five Basic Elements. "Yin" and "Yang" represent aspects of nature that are both opposite and complementary. Yin is "dark" and Yang is "light." Yin is "cold" and Yang is "hot." The theory of Five Basic Elements further postulates that natural phenomena can be categorized in terms of five basic elements: Metal, Wood, Water, Fire and Earth.[8]

There are Yin syndromes and there are Yang syndromes. There are Fire Organs and there are Metal Organs. Almost all of Chinese anatomy, physiology and pathology can be described as the interaction of these simple philosophical terms.

Finally, whereas Western definitions are focused and precise, Chinese concepts are vague and non-specific. Yin and Yang, for example, are conceived as broad, over-arching categories of nature. Even things like Chinese herbs seem vague and unrefined. Herbal remedies include such items as ginseng, cinnamon and mint. There is no list of 25 similar-sounding antibiotics, all with slightly different structures and chemical properties.

I paused for a moment to think. It was the same human body. The desire to diagnose and treat disease seemed more or less the same. But the two medicines, for whatever reason, had developed along two entirely different paths.

The sun was ending its descent into the horizon. The bus had reached the monastery. We entered through an ornate gate, and several monks in long silk gowns came out to greet us. Chinese medicine was the perfect example for understanding the Chinese way of thinking. The difference in thinking between Western and Chinese medicine, I hypothesized, was the linguistic difference between English and Chinese. Each language, in some unforeseen way, had influenced the development of its respective medicine. As I was to eventually learn, hidden deep within the mind of ancient Chinese medicine, lay the elusive connection between language and thought.

## -- 2 --
## The Chinese Character;
## The Difference between English and Chinese

Once arriving in China, Chinese characters fascinated me. They were the commonplace elements of everyday life, appearing on street signs, storefronts and Chinese menus. Yet they were also objects of enjoyment and veneration, gracefully exhibited in pictures and paintings. Each character had a unique personality, as well as a certain presence and permanence.

Early characters were like pictures, visual images of the objects they represented. The character for "fish" looked like a fish. The character for "man" looked like a man. As history progressed, characters became more abstract. They became more like symbols than pictures, so much that it would be impossible to determine the meaning of an unknown character just by looking at it.

Most characters could be analyzed into parts. The arrangement of these parts reflected the character's complex history and often indicated the character's pronunciation or meaning. Yet once formed, regardless of the history of the character's formation, the structure of the character never changed. No matter how the character was used within the sentence--as a noun, verb, adjective or adverb--the written form remained the same. You would never add a line or subtract a line, for example. Despite their visual complexity, characters came and went as immutable wholes. The structure of characters was permanent.

I was sitting on a crowded bus on my way back to the university, when I fell into conversation with a young Chinese woman. I remember that she was fashionably dressed, with long-braided hair and thin-wire glasses. We talked about the weather, the crowded city bus, and whether or not I had grown accustomed to Chinese food. Then the conversation turned to language.

"The way I see it," I explained, "the letters of the English alphabet represent the sounds of spoken speech. If you sound out the letters 'b,' 'i,' 'r,' 'd,' they represent the spoken word, 'bird.' The letters themselves have no particular meaning. They just tell you the pronunciation."

I wasn't much of a linguist, but the argument seemed compelling, so I continued.

"In Chinese, on the other hand, the 'character' is like a picture. The character for bird is an abstract representation of a real bird. It communicates meaning directly. Characters may make the language easier to read for a Chinese person, but they make the language almost impossible to learn as a foreigner."

Outside the window the mass of humanity was selling its wares and shopping. Horns blared and people shouted. Flimsy bicycles weaved in and out among buses and industrial trucks.

The young woman nodded, but I could tell she wasn't convinced. "I agree that the English alphabet is phonetic," she said. "The letters just represent sounds. But the Chinese characters are also phonetic."

She continued, "English letters represent spoken sounds, usually less than one syllable. Chinese characters also represent sound, but they represent the syllable as a whole. Every spoken syllable in Chinese is written with a separate Chinese character. But unlike English, every syllable in Chinese also has a meaning. So a written character represents a spoken syllable that also has a meaning. That's why it sometimes seems like characters represent meaning directly."

I was more confused than ever.

"The real difference between English and Chinese," she continued, "is that English looks for the difference between things. Chinese looks for the connection."

"Connection?"

"In English, for example, you have different words for different types of vehicles: 'Train,' 'bus,' 'car' or 'bicycle.' In Chinese, however, we only have one word, 'che,' meaning 'vehicle.' If I need to give you more information, I just tell you what type of 'che' it is: Train is a 'huo'-*che* ('fire'-*che*). Car is a 'qi'-*che* ('gas'-*che*). Bicycle is a 'zi-xing'-*che* ('self-go'-*che*)."

I was beginning to see the pattern. "Is a bus a *che*?"

"A bus is a *che*."

"Is a wheelbarrow a *che*?"

"A wheelbarrow is a *che*."

"Is an airplane a *che*?"

"An airplane is not a *che*. An airplane is a '*ji*.'"

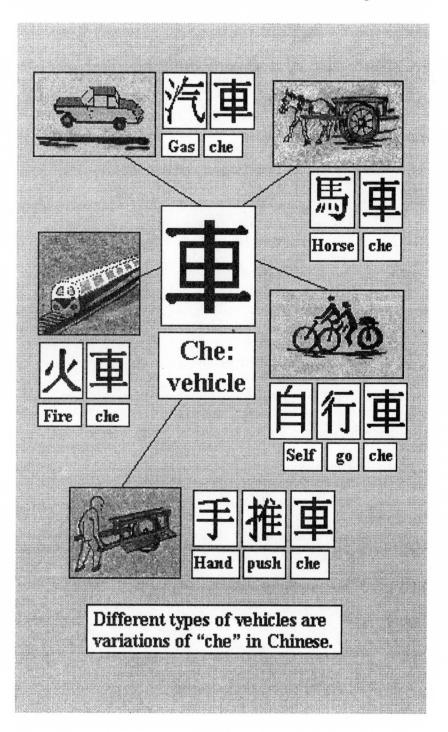

汽車 Gas che

馬車 Horse che

車 Che: vehicle

火車 Fire che

自行車 Self go che

手推車 Hand push che

Different types of vehicles are variations of "che" in Chinese.

## -- 3 --
## The Number of Chinese Characters;
## A Brief History of China

As foreign students we lived in the visiting student dormitory. It was a large, faceless building, conveniently located in the center of campus. The floors were made from cold concrete, and the rooms were sparsely furnished, but each morning we received a steaming pot of fresh hot water which gave a decidedly home-felt touch. There was a modest cafeteria, a weight-lifting room and a lounge for meeting with people. There was a giant courtyard for practicing *qi gong*, a Chinese form of exercise, some gymnastic bars, a shaded garden and a gargantuan rack for storing bicycles.

There were students there from all over the world: Europe, Japan and the United States. People studied Chinese for different reasons: business, translation, history and medicine. One of our favorite pastimes was discussing how many Chinese characters we knew. I figured I could read and write about 200-300 Chinese characters. Others knew around 500. At least one student knew over a thousand.

I soon discovered, however, that although there were approximately 50,000 Chinese characters in the language overall, far fewer were in common use. For example, approximately 5,000 characters were required to read a Chinese newspaper. The others had obscure, philosophical meanings and were rarely ever seen.

I was sitting in class one day, thinking about the multitude of Chinese characters, when I began to wonder if there were any new ones. After all, in English, there are new words. It seemed like a reasonable question, so I asked our instructor, Professor Wei.

"Truthfully," she said, after pausing for a moment, "There are no new characters."

"No new characters?"

Wei Jiao Shou or Professor Wei was a 30 year-old woman with a ruby complexion and a hearty laugh. She was descended from the Manchus, a group of ancient nomadic warriors who had invaded China, to which she attributed her robust nature and her love for life. With the discipline of a drill sergeant, she would repeat the same sentence over and over until everyone got it right. I don't remember ever falling asleep. In fact, after class, I would continue to hear her voice inside my head.

"No," she repeated firmly, "No new characters."

She began to clean the board. "There were always more Chinese characters than could be found in the official dictionaries," she started, considering the question as she wiped off the chalk. "That's because different regions used different characters as local people coined new terms. Furthermore, throughout history, Chinese literature provided a continual source of new characters. In fact, one role of the official dynastic 'dictionary-writers' was to determine which characters were 'new' and should be accepted into the official dictionaries, and which characters were merely variations of older ones.

"The first Chinese script was the *jia gu wen,* or oracle bone writing of the Shang Dynasty, in which oracles would make predictions based on inscriptions carved into turtle shells. Since that time there has been a gradual increase in the number of Chinese characters. The *Kang Xi Dictionary* of the Qing Dynasty was completed in 1716 and is considered the definitive dictionary of the Chinese language. It contains 47,035 characters."

The rest of the students had left for the cafeteria. Professor Wei gathered her books and we exited the building into the courtyard. As we walked she continued, "Let me see if I can explain this better."

"There are ten major Chinese dynasties," she started, "The Xia, Shang, Zhou, Qin, Han, Tang, Song, Yuan, Ming and Qing. After the Qing, you have the founding of the Republic of China in 1912 and the end of Imperial China.

"Think of Chinese dynasties like beads along a string--distinct segments of time, separated in between by brief periods of war and instability. Each Chinese dynasty is regarded as a single, homogenous unit. Over the course of the dynasties, the number of characters gradually increased.[9,10]

"The Xia Dynasty was mostly legendary," she continued, "So most people begin with the Shang (traditionally 1650 to 1027 BC)." That's when tribes north of the Yangtze became united under one rule. The Shang is known for its skill in bronze casting, as well as its *jia gu wen* or oracle bone inscriptions. The oracle bone inscriptions contain **4,000 to 5,000** characters.

"Following the Shang comes the Zhou (1027 to 256 BC), the "Classical Age" of Chinese philosophy. Here Confucius (551-479 BC) developed his many ideas regarding the hierarchical structure of family and state.

"The Zhou then deteriorated into the Seven Warring States, from which arose, in 221 BC, the 'Shi Huang Di' or 'First Emperor' of Imperial China. That marks the Qin Dynasty, contemporary with the Roman Empire in the West. The First Emperor created a unified script, built roads, dug waterways and started work on China's Great Wall, the thousand-mile barrier against the threat of invasion from the North."

"And after the Qin?" I asked.

"After the Qin Dynasty, comes the Han.[11] There you have the expansion of China and development of trade between China and Rome. Then, in AD 220, the Han Dynasty collapsed into a period of chaos and disunity in which three kingdoms; the Wu, the Wei and the Shu, all competed for control of the empire. *Shuo Wen Jie Zi* or *Explanation of Graphs* was written in the late Han and contains **9,353** characters."

In the courtyard, workers busily constructed what appeared to be a new café. Students rushed in every direction. A young couple sat on a bench, quietly talked and ate.

"After the Han comes the Tang (AD 618-906)," she continued, "the 'Golden Age'[12] of Chinese civilization. The Tang is known for its

28

architecture, music, painting and poetry, including the famous Tang poets, Wang Wei, Li Bo and Du Fu. The *Yu Pian Dictionary* was completed in AD 543 and contains **16,917** characters.

"Then comes the Song,[13] the 'Age of Chinese Maturity.'[14] The continual threat of invasion forced the Chinese culture inward.[15] You have Song landscape painting as well as the art of blue-green porcelain. The *Guang Yun Dictionary* dated 1011 contains **26,194** characters."

"And after the Song?" I asked. Each dynasty, its own separate unit, passed like a giant, uniform segment of time. The number of characters was gradually increasing.

"After the Song comes the Yuan (1279-1368), the first Chinese dynasty to be ruled by non-Chinese. The Mongols were a northern tribe, commanded by the notoriously brutal Genghis Khan. With their mobile cavalry and skill in archery they conquered China in 1279.

"The Yuan dynasty was replaced by the Ming (1368-1644), when the peasant Zhu Yuan Zhang rose from poverty to defeat the Mongols. Zhang placed the capital in Nanjing. His son moved the capital to Beijing. The Forbidden City was built, the Great Wall was expanded, and white-blue porcelain became the dynasty's standard. The *Zui Hui*

*Dictionary* of the Ming Dynasty was published in 1375," she said. "**33,179** characters."

"And finally," she said, "We come to the Qing, the last dynasty of Imperial China. The Qing was established in 1644 when the Manchus seized Beijing from the Northeast. It became the second rule of China by non-Chinese. However, with a rapid increase in the population and increasing pressure from abroad, the Qing Dynasty, as well as the traditional system of Chinese government, eventually collapsed. Sun Yat-sen (1866-1925), a Western-educated doctor of medicine, overthrew the Manchus in 1911 and in 1912 established the Republic of China. The *Kang Xi Dictionary* of the Qing Dynasty was published in 1716 and is considered the definitive dictionary of the Chinese language. **47,035** characters!"

We arrived at the cafeteria. I was exhausted. My head was buzzing from the magnitude of Chinese history as I tried to imagine 47,000 characters and if there was anyone who could possibly remember them. "So what happens now when you have a new Chinese character?" I asked.

She paused for a moment. "Well, except for local variants and a few technical terms, all of the characters used today date from 1716, the publication of the *Kang Xi*. Otherwise, there are no new Chinese characters."[16]

"No new characters?"

"No."

"But there must be new characters. After all, what does Chinese do for new vocabulary?"

She thought for a moment. "There are no new Chinese characters," she said finally. "There are only new character combinations."[17]

"Combinations?"

But by that time, the food had arrived and everyone was ready to eat.

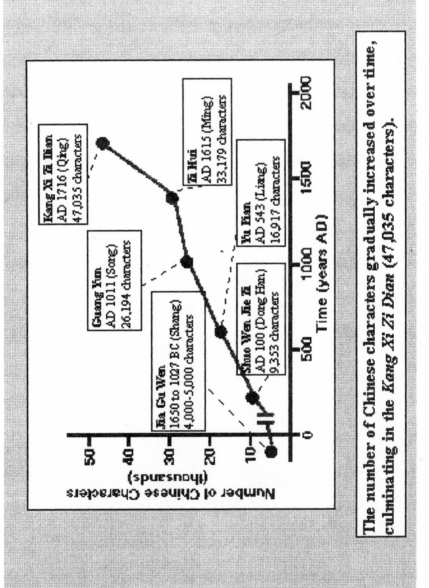

The number of Chinese characters gradually increased over time, culminating in the *Kang Xi Zi Dian* (47,035 characters).

## -- 4 --
## Character Combinations
## and the Art of Chinese Stir-fry


The notion of "combinations" is really the key concept in understanding the Chinese language. Generally speaking, the "character combination" is the linguistic equivalent of the English concept of "word." That is, it is the unit of language most commonly used to represent a single meaning or a single idea.[18] However, whereas words in English are phonetically unique, represented by their own unique sequence of letters, Chinese uses combinations of more simple-sounding characters. A small number of characters can be used to make a much greater number of character combinations.

As previously discussed, the different names of vehicles in English are variations of *che* in Chinese: "train"--"fire-*che*," "car"--"vapor-*che*," "bicycle"--"self-go-*che*." You begin to see the pattern. A "wheelbarrow" in Chinese is a "hand-push-*che*." A "carriage" in Chinese is a "four-wheel-horse-*che*." In similar fashion, different types of machines in Chinese are different variations of *-ji* (machine). "Telephone" in Chinese is an "electric-talk-machine." "Air conditioner" in Chinese is an "air-mix-machine."

But character combinations in Chinese go beyond the naming of objects. Combinations extend to grammar as well. For example, in order to express grammatical meaning, English words will change in sound. "Car" becomes "cars" when it changes in number. The verb "watch" becomes "watched" when it changes in tense. This change in sound, reflecting a change in meaning, is known as "inflection." A word's inflectional form depends on its grammatical role in the sentence. Deriving the correct inflectional form is a matter of learning the "rules": I watch, I *watched*; I talk, I *talked*.[19] As English has a phonetic alphabet, a change in the word's sound is appropriately represented by a change in the word's spelling.

But Chinese characters don't inflect. Within any given dialect, they are always the same written symbol and the same spoken sound. In Chinese, grammatical meaning is expressed by the combination.

Whereas English has "car" and "cars," Chinese has "car" and "very many car" (*che* and *hen duo che*). The character *che*, 車, meaning "car," remains unchanged, whether singular or plural.

In English, the past tense of "watch" is "watched." In Chinese, the past tense of "watch" (*kan*) is "yesterday watch" (*zuo tian kan*). Again, in Chinese, no matter how many people are watching, whether they watch today, yesterday or tomorrow, the character *kan*, 看, meaning "watch," remains unchanged in both sound and spelling.

Chinese linguist Bernhard Karlgren explains this concept:

> It is a well-known fact that Indo-European languages express variations in one and the same word by means of various inflectional affixes. If we compare the forms puella [meaning "girl, young woman"], puellae, pullam, puella(-), puellas, puellarum, puellis, we find that they all possess an element puell-, bearing a sense common to them all, but they differ in having affixes of various forms.

He continues,

> Chinese does all of its work with monosyllable materials.[20]

The notion of "combination" is the key concept in understanding Chinese vocabulary and grammar. But combinations occur elsewhere in

Chinese culture--in poetry, painting and literature. Most noticeably, they occur in Chinese cooking.

Of course, combinations occur in all types of cooking: in Italian pasta, Mexican fajitas or in a Western-style salad or omelet. Combinations, however, occur most prominently in Chinese. Consider, for example, Chinese stir-fry, the fast-paced method of frying meats and vegetables over very intense heat. Depending on the dish, different ingredients--chicken, beef, vegetables and noodles--are added to the mix in rapid sequence, energetically stirred and completed in minutes.

To the uninitiated, stir-fry may seem like a fast, delicious, but random assortment of meats and vegetables. In fact, each dish is a carefully conceived combination. Each ingredient's flavor, fragrance, color, texture and shape complements every other ingredient in a complex sensory whole.

Yu Xiang Chicken, for example, is a popular dish from northern China. Recipes vary, but the dish generally consists of chicken, scallions, celery, dried mushrooms and dried red peppers--all stir-fried in a spicy ginger-garlic sauce.

First there is the **flavor** and **aroma**, provided by the ginger, garlic, scallions and dried red pepper. Next, there is the **color**: chicken is white, mushrooms are black, red pepper is red, and celery and scallions are green. Next, there is the **texture**: Chicken is tender; mushrooms, celery and scallions are crisp. Finally, there is the **shape**: The vegetables are cut into slivers to echo the chicken cut into slivers. The final product, a pleasing arrangement of flavors, colors, textures and shape is eaten over a fluffy bed of white rice.[21]

"Combinations" can also be seen in the Chinese meal viewed as a whole. For example, when eating in a Western restaurant, each person orders separately from the menu and then eats his own separate meal. In China, the meal is served "family style," with the dishes all placed at the center of the table. Everyone has a bowl of rice, and picks and chooses from the selection at hand. Each dish contributes something to the whole. One dish is spicy and another is bland. One dish is pork and another is beef. Overall, there is a balanced combination of contrasting meats, flavors, colors and cooking styles.[22] The number of dishes roughly equals the number of people eating.

Westerners eat with a fork and a knife, used for cutting large pieces of food. In China, food is eaten with chopsticks. All food comes to the table in ready-to-eat, bite-size morsels. Chopsticks may not be good for cutting or separating, but seem particularly well-suited to picking up one-at-a-time, the small, isolated pieces.

Slivers go with slivers, slices go with slices, and cubes go with cubes. Of course, the size of the pieces must be uniform. Uniform cuts allow for more even cooking. Otherwise, small pieces will be overcooked and large pieces will be undercooked.[23]

Finally, in Chinese cooking, it is interesting that a single type of instrument can be used in many different ways. Western kitchens, for example, have innumerable knives, utensils, pots and pans, each with its own special purpose. There is a "bread knife" for bread, a "cheese knife" for cheese and a "steak knife" for steak. You wouldn't cut steak with a bread knife, and you wouldn't fry an egg in a pot.[24] Chinese kitchens, alternatively, have few instruments. All cutting and crushing is performed with a cleaver.[25] All boiling and stir-frying is performed in the wok. One instrument has many different applications.

So in a way, preparing Chinese stir-fry is like creating Chinese vocabulary. The small, uniform segments of food are like the assortment of Chinese characters. You can have chicken with mushrooms and snow peas, or you can have the beef with snow peas and scallions. The same ingredients are combined and recombined to create an infinite variety of different dishes.

# Stir-fry with Chopsticks

## -- 5 --
## Relationship among Chinese Characters;
## Philosophy of Confucius

Of all the students in the program, Thomas was the most enigmatic. An American born to Japanese immigrants, Thomas spent the first 25 years of his adult life living within the mountains in a monastery in Japan. In fact, Thomas would have continued to live in the monastery, had he not needed to care for his aging parents. Returning to the United States, he completed a doctorate in Chinese and Japanese philosophy, and took a position as a university professor. Now on break, he was studying the Chinese language for the first time.

Thomas was a brilliant man. He was fluent in both English and Japanese, and was familiar with the writings of innumerable philosophers. He also seemed to have a profound understanding of life itself.

His wardrobe consisted of only two different robes. There was one for everyday use, and one for special occasions. His head was completely shaved, a ritual he performed every day promptly at 5 a.m. His only other apparel was a pair of wooden shoes, which made a distinct hollow sound when he walked down the corridor.

He was always even-tempered, taking everything as it came. He never seemed rushed, excited or annoyed. And then there was his smile, easily his most distinctive feature. It seemed that everything for Thomas was a source of interest or entertainment.

"The mind is like a mirror," he said. "One must always keep it clean of dust. Eat when you are hungry, sleep when you are tired. Experience the goodness and the beauty of life in every detail."[26]

Sometimes late at night, when the others were out or going to sleep, I would explain my ideas on language and thought and the problem of finding a good example. He once explained, "The self is confused by outside forces. Understanding the truth depends entirely on yourself. Rid yourself of all prior judgments--good and bad, gain and loss. Transcend absolutes, and you may ultimately discover your true self.[27]

"In the city, the mind is confused by noise and pollution. At the top of the mountain, the mind can run free. As you will someday learn, the principle of things is not in some far-off land or imaginary circumstance, but in your own mind."[28]

Thomas knew lots of Chinese characters. In fact, he knew more than any other student. That was because during the Tang Dynasty (AD 618-906), the Japanese people adopted the Chinese characters to use to write the Japanese language. Prior to that time, Japanese was strictly a spoken language, with no accepted way of writing. Fluent in Japanese, Thomas was naturally able to read and write the Chinese characters.

But interestingly, like the rest of us, Thomas knew very little Chinese. He only knew the Japanese translation. And most strikingly, even though he knew the meaning of the individual characters, he didn't know the meaning of the combinations.

That is because the meaning of the combination is something much greater than the meaning of the individual characters. Language is a system of representation. Sounds represent ideas that already exist in our heads. Knowing that an object is a "vertical-rise-machine," for example, tells you very little about the meaning of the object. You need to see a helicopter, ride a helicopter or read about a helicopter before you can understand its meaning. A "vertical-rise-machine" might just as easily be an elevator.

As previously discussed, Chinese characters can be recombined to make an infinite variety of combinations. I soon realized, however, that combinations are not simply random assortments of different characters. Rather, like ingredients in a platter of stir-fry, within the combination, there is a specific relationship among the individual parts.

Consider *zhi-sheng-ji* or "vertical-rise-machine," the Chinese equivalent of the English word, "helicopter." Implicit within the combination, "machine" is the main character. It indicates the overall category of the object being discussed. "Vertical-rise," on the other hand, is supportive. It modifies "machine." It more specifically indicates the type of machine. In addition to a *vertical-rise*-machine, for example, there are other types of machines. There is a *shou-yin*-machine (*accept-sound*-machine or "radio"), a *tuo-la*-machine (*drag-pull*-machine or "tractor"), as well as a *ge-cao*-machine, which is a machine that cuts grass.

Furthermore, "*vertical-rise*" itself is a combination of characters. "Vertical" indicates the direction of "rise." Therefore "rise" is the main character and "vertical" is supportive.

"Vertical-rise-machine" is an example of what may be considered a "hierarchical combination"--that is, a combination of characters in which there is a hierarchical relationship among the individual parts. However, there are other types of combinations as well. Linguist Yuen Ren Chao in his book, *A Grammar of Spoken Chinese*, outlines several major categories of character combinations.[29]

"Subordinative compounds" most closely resemble the "hierarchical" combinations previously discussed. "Antonym compounds" occur when two characters with opposite meaning are placed together. "Da-xiao" ("big-small"), for example, means "size." "Chang-duan" ("long-short") means "length." Alternatively, "Synonym compounds" occur when characters with similar meaning are placed together. "Qing-chu" ("clear-distinct") means "clear." "Sheng-yin" ("noise-tone") means "sound." Additionally, there are Subject-Predicate combinations, Verb-Object combinations, Prefixes and Suffixes, and Reduplications. Each classification implies a different type of "relationship" that exists among the characters in the combination.

Thomas and I were in the student lounge, relaxing one day after class, when I once again expressed my interest in the possible connection between language and thought.

"It's in the hierarchy of the characters," he said.

"Hierarchy of the characters?"

"Yes," he continued, "The Chinese way of thinking--the structure of their families, the structure of their government--it all seems to follow from the hierarchy of the characters."

I failed to understand.

"Are you familiar with the philosophy of Confucius?" he asked.

"Somewhat," I replied. Confucius was China's most famous philosopher, born during the Zhou Dynasty. In class, we had discussed his ideas several times.

"Confucius influenced Chinese culture more than any other philosopher,"[30] started Thomas. "He was born in 551 BC to an aristocratic family and was originally employed in the civil service. But he became frustrated with what he viewed as an immoral society, so he resigned from his post and set out to create a new model for social and political order. None of his writings exist to this day. His ideas are best known through the *Lun Yu* or *Confucian Analects*, a collection of his sayings compiled by his students.

"Confucian philosophy is a social philosophy, concerned with the organization of people in society. The Confucian model is a really complex prescription for the proper relation between individuals. It is based on the feudal hierarchy of the Zhou Dynasty, as well as the time-honored structure of the traditional Chinese family."[31]

Thomas considered for a moment and then continued.

"Generally speaking, American culture is predicated on the individual. A high cultural value placed on self-expression and self-reliance. From an early age, children are taught that they are 'different' and 'unique,' and they are encouraged to develop their 'individuality.' Children may pursue their own interests and aspirations, even if it goes against the wishes of their parents. If anything, parents should learn to be more 'open-minded.'

"But in ancient China, individual predilections played a minor role. All value and importance was placed on the family.

"Only a small proportion of the population lived in cities. People lived in villages, where life revolved around cultivation of the land. The production of rice, the major component of the Chinese diet, required a tremendous amount of physical labor. Bending over at the waist, laborers would tread backwards through ankle-deep water and plant rice seedlings one at a time. In the ensuing months when the rice was ripe, the fields were drained and the rice was harvested. Everything was done by hand.

"There was flooding and there was famine. There was disease and there was war. But the individual was never alone. It was the family and not the individual that took economic responsibility.[32]

"The traditional Chinese family consisted of a highly organized system of kinship relations. People were not individuals in the Western sense, with personal needs and desires. Rather, people played prescribed roles, traditionally defined, that had been passed down from generation to generation.[33]

"At the top of the hierarchy was the father, with full control over the family income. The father could arrange the marriage of his children and decide on their future professions.[34] However, the father was also responsible to the ancestors in Heaven. Performing the proper ancestral rituals was his responsibility.

"The role of the wife was to manage the household and raise the children. The role of the son was 'filial piety' or loyalty to his parents. It was his utmost duty that his parents suffer no want, sorrow or anxiety.[35] Daughters were also expected to be loyal to their parents, but they would be married into other families and their role was less important.

"The larger family unit consisted of three to four generations, all living together in the same compound. Again, familial relations followed a traditional order. Older generations ranked above younger generations. Men ranked above women.

"Each different relationship carried a specific identifying term. For example, there was no one term for the English word, 'uncle.' It made a difference whether the person was on your father's or your mother's side, and whether he was your father's older brother ('bo bo') or your father's younger brother ('shu shu'). In fact, the *Er Ya Dictionary* of the Han Dynasty contains over one hundred terms describing the different familial relationships.[36]

"Each specific relationship had a standardized behavior and mode of address. Each person within the family knew precisely where he stood in relation to everyone else. In fact, individuals were often not addressed by their name, but rather, by the title of their role."[37]

Thomas continued, "Although roles were fixed by convention, in a sense, individuals were not. Each individual played more than one role, depending on the social context. For example, similar to Western culture, the same person could be a 'father,' an 'uncle' or a 'younger brother.'

"But even though individuals could play different roles, focus was always on the family. When individuals achieved greatness, it was for the glory of the family.[38] A younger sibling, no matter how successful, was always respectful of his elder siblings.[39] The father, although chief, answered to the ancestors in Heaven."

I leaned back in my chair. The hierarchical structure of the Chinese family was certainly interesting. Within the family, each individual played a different role, and there were specific relationships among the different individuals. "But what does the structure of the Chinese family have to do with the philosophy of Confucius?" I asked.

Thomas continued, "Confucius used this structure of the traditional Chinese family as the basis for his model for social and political life.

"In Confucius's model of society there were five cardinal relationships, the W*u-Lun*: Q*in* (Affection) between parent and child, *Yi* (Righteousness) between ruler and subject, *Bie* (Distinction) between husband and wife, *Xu* (Order) between old and young and *Xin* (Sincerity) between friends.[40]

"According to Confucius, each person must play his proper role. 'Let the ruler be a ruler, the father be a father and the son be a son,'[41] said Confucius. This, he believed, was the key to social harmony.

"'*Li*,' meaning 'propriety,' was the central concept of Confucian philosophy.[42, 43] It meant acting in a manner suitable to one's social position. There was a complex code of etiquette and ceremony, depending on the specific social relationship: father-son, teacher-student or ruler-subject. '*Ren*' was 'benevolence' or 'overcoming one's selfish desires and acting in accordance with propriety.' '*Xiao*' was filial piety or 'fulfilling the spirit of propriety with regard to one's parents.'[44,45] '*Xiu Shen*' was 'self-cultivation.' However, it wasn't 'self-cultivation' in the Western sense of developing one's 'individuality.' It was 'self-cultivation' into the accepted roles and relationships that would provide for the overall harmony of the group.[46]

"Confucius's political ideas were an extension of his social philosophy.[47] After his death, his teachings became widely popular, and the Emperor Wu, in establishing the Han Dynasty, adopted Confucian teaching as the official state doctrine.

"At the peak of the pyramid sat the Emperor, who received his legitimacy to rule from the ancestors in Heaven. The bestowal of this 'Mandate of Heaven' was temporal and conditional, dependent on the moral qualification of the ruler.[48] An immoral ruler would lose the legitimacy to rule, and the 'Mandate of Heaven' would be transferred to the next ruling dynasty.

"Below the Emperor sat the 'bureaucratic' administration of Confucian scholars. The Confucian bureaucracy was a hierarchy of individuals responsible for organizing and directing the various affairs of state. Officials were trained in the Confucian classics. Unlike the feudal system of the prior Zhou Dynasty in which positions in government were hereditary, Confucian scholars achieved their position through a rigorous standardized exam.

"Spread out over the country was a giant network of divisions. In the Qing Dynasty, for example, provinces were divided into circuits (*dao*), circuits were divided into prefectures (*fu*), and prefectures were divided into districts (*xian*). Then, populating the districts were the villages (*cun*), consisting of 50-500 families. Each prefecture, circuit and district consisted of appointed officials, responsible to their superiors. The Emperor had the final decision on any important matter.

"Yet although the government was centralized, the villages themselves were autonomous.[50,51] For example, each village provided for its own food, education and defense. Villages were governed by elders, chosen for their wisdom and experience. Villages could punish their members, and they could enter into treaties with other villages. Furthermore, because they governed themselves, villagers were

*Li*, translated as "propriety" or "good manners," is the central concept of Confucian philosophy.

particularly resentful of outside intervention. They preferred to be given an mandate, and then they themselves choose the best mode of action.[51]

"So on one hand, in order to maintain the authority to rule, the Emperor was responsible for the happiness of the people. Neglecting the people would lead to a loss of the Mandate and a transfer of political power. On the other hand, given the changing needs of the empire, the Emperor could depend on the loyalty and cooperation of his constituents. This hierarchical system of government, despite the rise and fall of the various Chinese dynasties, provided the stable structure of Chinese political life for over two thousand years."

And then I understood. "You're right," I said, "It's in the characters. The philosophy of Confucius is there in the characters.

"The hierarchical structure of Confucian thought parallels the hierarchical structure of the Chinese characters," I continued. "The manner in which Confucius organized the members of the group, for example, describing their roles and their inter-relationships, almost exactly coincides with the organization of characters within combinations. Each person plays a role within the Chinese family. The meaning of the family, however, is greater than the meaning of the individual members. In a similar way, each Chinese character contributes meaning to the combination. Yet the meaning of the combination is greater than the meaning of the parts. Family members change their role depending on the specific relationship. Likewise, Chinese characters change their meaning depending on the combination."

Thomas smiled broadly and gently nodded his head. "Excellent," he said. "Remember, if there is a connection between language and thought, then it must exist within each of our minds. Free your mind, and you may discover the connection, yet."

## -- 6 --
## Chinese Medicine and Correlative Thinking

The connection between language and thought, I imagined, lay somewhere in the mind of ancient Chinese medicine. The Chinese physicians, in pursuit of the health of their patients, had developed a sophisticated system of physiology, pathology, diagnosis and treatment, completely outside the realm of Western medical science. It was a system of thought that had its own form of logic, which the famous Chinese historian Joseph Needham termed, "correlative thinking." This notion of "correlative thinking," I decided, provided an excellent starting point for understanding the unique organization of Chinese medical thought.

In his monumental series of books, *Science and Civilisation in China*, Needham explains that there are two main theories of traditional Chinese medicine: The Theory of Yin-Yang and the Theory of Five Basic Elements. These theories are most classically described in the ancient Chinese book, *The Emperor's Classic of Internal Medicine* (*Huang Di Nei Jing*), written during the Han Dynasty.

The first theory, the Theory of Yin-Yang, postulates two separate forces of nature, Yin and Yang. These two forces are opposite and complimentary, and correspond to various qualities of the universe: Yin is dark, cold and wet. Yang is light, hot and dry. Yin and Yang then interact via various established "relationships." There is the relationship of "consuming-increasing" as well as the relationship of "mutual-transforming."[53] In this manner, Yin and Yang work to animate all objects and phenomenon in the universe.

The second theory, the Theory of Five Basic Elements, is much more involved. Whereas Yin-Yang postulates two separate forces, Five Elements postulates five general categories: Metal, Wood, Water, Fire and Earth. The Five Elements are not substances in the chemical sense, but rather, are broad, over-arching categories of nature.

The Five Elements correspond to qualities of the universe that also come in groups of five. For example, there are Five Colors (White, Green, Black, Red and Yellow) and Five Flavors (Pungent,[54] Sour, Salty, Bitter and Sweet). Each Color or Flavor then corresponds to (or "is

correlated with") one of the Five Basic Elements: Green to Wood, Red to Fire, Yellow to Earth, White to Metal and Black to Water.

Furthermore, similar to Yin-Yang, the Five Elements interact according to several inter-Element "relationships." For example, there is the relationship of "Mutual Generation," in which Wood generates Fire, Fire generates Earth, Earth generates Metal, Metal generates Water, and Water generates Wood. These relationships then also apply to the other groups of five. Hence, Green generates Red, Red generates Yellow, Yellow generates White, White generates Black, and Black generates Green. In addition to "Mutual Generation," there are relationships of "Mutual Subjugation" and "Counter Subjugation," as well.

The arrangement of Five Elements is similar to the childhood game of "Rock, Paper, Scissors," in which three separate elements--rock, paper and scissors--all interact via specific relationships: the **rock** breaks the scissors, the **scissors** cut the paper, and the **paper** smothers the rock. This sequence of rock-scissors-paper-rock would then correspond to one of the "relationships" of the Theory of Five Elements.

Hence, the Theory of Five Elements is a complex network that describes the inter-relationship among various qualities of the universe.

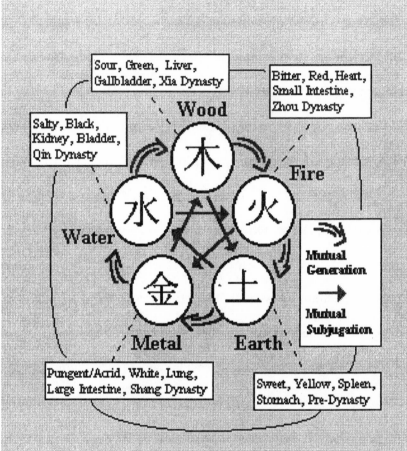

Sour, Green, Liver, Gallbladder, Xia Dynasty

Bitter, Red, Heart, Small Intestine, Zhou Dynasty

Salty, Black, Kidney, Bladder, Qin Dynasty

木 Wood

水 Water

火 Fire

金 Metal

土 Earth

Mutual Generation

Mutual Subjugation

Pungent/Acrid, White, Lung, Large Intestine, Shang Dynasty

Sweet, Yellow, Spleen, Stomach, Pre-Dynasty

# The Theory of Five Elements

It is this system of thought, with its various "correlations," that Needham

terms "correlative thinking." He writes,

> [Correlative thinking] has its own causality and its own
> logic. It is not either superstition or primitive superstition,
> but a characteristic thought-form of its own...[54]
>
> The symbolic correlations...all formed part of one colossal
> pattern. Things behaved in particular ways...because of their
> position in the ever-moving cyclical universe...Things in the
> universe which belonged to the same classes (e.g. east,
> wood, green, wind, wheat) resonated with, or energized,
> each other...It was part of a very closely knit universe in
> which only things of certain class would affect other things
> of the same class...It was a picture of an extremely and
> precisely ordered universe, in which things 'fitted'...so
> exactly that you could not insert a hair between them.[55]

According to legend, the Theory of Five Elements was originally

described in the Early Han Dynasty (2nd century BC) by the great

Chinese scholar, Tsou Yen.[56] Tsou Yen originally proposed the theory in

order to predict the seemingly chaotic succession of Chinese political

powers. He believed that each Chinese dynasty corresponded to a

different Element, and that dynasties followed one after another

according to the order of "Mutual Subjugation," in which Wood

subjugated Earth, Metal subjugated Wood, Fire subjugated Metal, Water

subjugated Fire, and Earth subjugated Water. As each of the Five

Elements subjugated in turn, each new dynasty succeeded by virtue of the newly reigning element. For example, the sequence Earth, Wood, Metal, Fire and Water represented the respective Elements of the Pre-Dynastic, Xia, Shang, Zhou and Qin Dynasties.

According to Tsou Yen's theory, a successful emperor needed to rule in accordance with the currently dominant Element. He needed build appropriate temples and perform appropriate rituals. By establishing his position within the scheme of Five Elements, he would convince people of his legitimacy.

Over the next couple of centuries, Tsou Yen's ideas grew in popularity. Then during the Late Han (AD 25 to AD 220), a wide range of schools adopted Tsou Yen's ideas with the purpose of explaining various phenomena. It was at this time that Chinese physicians applied the Theory of Five Basic Elements to the field of Chinese medicine.

The Chinese physicians recognized that the human body could be divided groups of five. There were Five Senses and Five Tissues. After some debate, it was determined that there were 5 *Zang* organs ("storage facilities" or "depots") and 6 *Fu* organs ("grain collection centers" or "palaces."[57]). The 6th Fu organ or "Triple Burner"[58] was considered as a separate entity, so as far as the system of five's was concerned, everything still fit.

The five Zang organs are the Heart, Lung, Spleen, Liver and Kidney. The six Fu organs are the Gall Bladder, Stomach, Large Intestine, Small Intestine, Urinary Bladder and Triple Burner. The Zang organs manufacture and store the bodily essences: *Qi*, Blood and Bodily Fluid. The Fu organs digest food, absorb nutrients and transmit waste.

The Zang and Fu organs each correspond to one of the Five Basic Elements. Consider the Zang: the **Heart** warms the body and corresponds to **Fire**. The **Spleen** transforms the essential substances and corresponds to **Earth**. The **Lungs** have properties of "clearing and descending" and correspond to **Metal**. The **Kidneys** control water metabolism and correspond to **Water**. Finally, the **Liver** controls the flow of *Qi* and corresponds to **Wood**.

The inter-organ relationships then follow directly from the Theory of Five Basic Elements: The **Kidneys** nourish the Liver. The **Liver** stores the blood that supports the Heart. The heat of the **Heart** warms the Spleen. The **Spleen** transforms the nutrients that replenish the Lungs. And finally, the clearing and descending function of the **Lungs** assists the downward flow of water by the **Kidneys**. More simply stated, Water-Wood-Fire-Earth-Metal-Water: Mutual Generation.

Of course, there are Mutual Subjugation and Counter Subjugation relationships, as well.

Each of Zang-Fu organs has a particular effect on the flow and "transformation" of *Qi*. The Spleen directs *Qi* upward. The Lung, Heart and Stomach direct *Qi* downward. Any dysfunction of the various organs disrupts the flow and transformation of *Qi*.

Finally, the concept of disease can be understood, in part, through the Theories of Yin-Yang and Five Basic Elements. Whereas Western medicine reduces disease to its cellular and biochemical components, Chinese diseases are like syndromes[59]--constellations of historical findings, physical signs and patient symptoms. Signs include those elicited via the ancient methods of tongue and pulse diagnosis. Symptoms include pain, nausea, vomiting, etc. Syndromes are associated with one of the Zang-Fu organs, or differentiated, among other methods, according to the Eight Principles of Syndrome Differentiation: Interior/Exterior, Cold/Heat, Deficiency/Excess, and Yin/Yang. Once the syndrome has been diagnosed, the appropriate treatment is applied.[60]

Hence, Needham's notion of "correlative thinking" neatly explains, at least from a Western perspective, the often confusing logic of

Yin-Yang and Five Basic Elements. Chinese medicine is indeed based on a very organized system of thought.

The theories of Yin-Yang and Five Basic Elements can be found in any Chinese medical textbook. The system of correlations and various relationships can be confirmed with any traditionally trained Chinese doctor. But, once again, why should there be two, such divergent ways of thinking? Why should one medicine think "scientifically," and the other think in "correlations"? The answer to that difficult question would require a late night session with Dr. Martin Chang.

Qi, translated as "Energy" or "Life Force," is a central concept in Chinese medicine.

## -- 7 --
## Conversation with Dr. Chang

"Herbs in China have an ancient history," said Dr. Chang as he took a long sip of tea. "But they are poorly understood. Before entering the Western medical school, I was trained by a famous traditional doctor, so I actually understand herbs quite well."

I nodded, observing a small bottle on his desk.

"Those are the herbs I prepared for a patient. Her pulse was fast and slippery, and her tongue was sticky-yellow. In Chinese medicine those are classic signs of Liver Damp-Heat. The herbs I prepared helped to soothe her Liver and assist her transformation of *Qi*."

I remembered reading about *Qi*, the bodily essence whose proper transformation was required for good health. It was possible to have too much or too little *Qi*, or to have it concentrated in all the wrong places. Performing *Qi gong*, a type of physical activity, is a conscious effort to manipulate the flow and function *Qi*.

"Depending on the location, *Qi* plays different roles. [61] Only when *Qi* flows freely, can it undergo the changes or transformations. Remember, your diet, your activities, your relationships--all of these influence the flow and transformation of *Qi*."

"So what do the herbs do?" I asked.

"Well, in order for *Qi* to function, each organ must perform its role. A healthful diet and balanced lifestyle help maintain the transformations. But when *Qi* is too strong, too weak, or moves in the wrong direction, Chinese herbs and acupuncture help restore the proper flow."

"Well, if Chinese herbs work so well, why are Western doctors reluctant to use them?"

He thought for a moment. "Western doctors are very open to new ideas. The problem is trying to combine two very different ways of thinking. Western medicine is founded on the theories of Western science, mainly physics, chemistry and biology. Chinese medicine, on the other hand, is founded on theories of Chinese philosophy, mainly Yin-Yang and Five Basic Elements."

He coughed to clear his throat. "Let me correct myself, because the *theory* of Chinese medicine and the *practice* of Chinese medicine are two slightly different things. The Theories of Yin-Yang and Five Basic

Elements first arose during the Han dynasty, about 2,000 years ago. But the practice of Chinese medicine, in the form of herbs and acupuncture, is really much older, attributed to the legendary emperor Shen Nong over 5,000 years ago.

"From a modern perspective, Chinese medicine is based on Yin-Yang and Five Basic Elements. From a historical perspective, however, Chinese medicine developed empirically, from practical experience. People discovered that certain herbs could be used to treat certain diseases. This knowledge was accumulated and passed from generation to generation. Only later, when people wanted a theoretical framework to understand how the herbs worked, did they adopt the theories of Chinese philosophy. Those theories had already been developed to explain other things, such as the succession of political dynasties. Chinese medicine was just a new application."

I considered his explanation. Numerous medications in Western medicine were initially discovered empirically. Western doctors have prescribed aspirin for many years. Only recently, however, have they understood aspirin's biochemical actions. "So in a sense," I offered, "At their earliest conception, Western and Chinese medicine were similar. Both were based on practical experience."

"Right, but later, when people tried to develop theories to explain their practical knowledge, the two traditions diverged. From then on, Western doctors tried to break everything apart. Chinese doctors tried to fit everything together."

"What do you mean?"

He laughed, "The Chinese way of thinking and the Western way of thinking are very different. It is difficult to explain. Western thinking tries to break things down into their fundamental components, and then develop principles or 'rules' that describe how the components interact.[62] That's why Western thinking eventually developed physics, chemistry and biology. Chinese thinking, on the other hand, tries to incorporate everything into a single, unified whole. That's why people call Chinese thinking 'holistic.'"

"But Western thought also developed several unified, cohesive models to explain health and disease. For example, what makes the Theory of Five Elements different from the Greek theory of Bodily Humors?"

"If I can remember correctly, the Hippocratic theory of Bodily Humors, from the 4th century BC, postulated that there were Four Bodily Humors: Blood, Bile, Black Bile and Phlegm."[63]

"Right," I said.

"On the surface, both theories have many interesting similarities. Both try to understand human health and disease in terms of a finite number of abstract categories. Disease is seen in terms of a deficiency or excess in the normal balance of Humors or *Qi*. Health is restored when that balance is returned, via herbs or other therapies.

"However, there is one important difference. The history of Western science is the history of one model or paradigm replacing another. New knowledge leads to a revision of the old model. For example, the Greek model of the human body was popular for many centuries, but was eventually replaced by the anatomic model, based on Vesalius's human dissections.[64] The Vesalius model was then further refined by the mechanistic models of the Renaissance.[65,66] Finally, with so many possible models, people designed experiments to determine which ones offered the best representation of the empirically observed phenomena.

"In the Chinese case, however, after the basic theories of Yin-Yang and Five Elements became solidified in approximately the 2nd century AD, the models never changed. Not in almost 2000 years. There may be different interpretations of the various relationships or even different attempts to incorporate data into the various categories, but the basic foundations of the theory never change. No one considers, for example, that there might be four elements or six elements. There are always just five. New knowledge is always interpreted in terms of the old model. The old model never changes.

"Let me give you an example. As we were discussing, the Chinese doctors of the Han Dynasty used the theories of Yin-Yang and Five Elements to develop an elaborate system describing the physiology and pathophysiology of the human body. The problem still existed, however, as how to explain the action of the Chinese herbs.

"Up to the point of the *Tai Su* (an early version of *Emperor's Classic of Internal Medicine* published during the Han Dynasty), the Chinese pharmaceutical literature contained only empirical descriptions of individual herbs. Textbooks explained which herbs should be used to treat which symptoms, but provided no explanation as to why such substances exhibited their particular effects.

"Hence, the *Tai Su*, in the chapter entitled "Regulating One's Diet," presents the first systematic categorization of food qualities according to the Theory of Five Elements. Each of the Five Grains, Five Fruits, Five Vegetables and Five Domestic Animals are described as having one of five colors (yellow, green, black, red and white) and one of five flavors (acrid, sweet, sour, bitter and salty). Then, via the lines of correspondence established by the Theory of Five Elements, each food quality is assigned a physiologic action (hardening, collecting, dissipating, calming and moistening) as well as a location of action (the Five Zang organs). This five-based categorization of food qualities provided a new conceptual tool for prescribing a healthy diet in accordance with the proper balance of Five Elements.[67]

"The ideas of the *Tai Su* were again considered in the *Su Wen*, the Tang Dynasty revision of the *Emperor's Classic*. But instead of food qualities, the discussion centered on herbs and the treatment of illness. Using the Theory of Five Elements and lines of correspondence, the *Su Wen* provided a new theoretical system that linked primary drug qualities (color, flavor and 'temperature'[68]) to the mode of physiologic action.[69] At this point in time, however, specific drug names were not discussed.

"It was then the goal of the Song and Yuan Dynasty physicians to verify this theoretical system against the known action of clinically used herbs. That is, using specific herbs as examples, they sought to compare the empirically observed effects with the effects predicted by the Theory of Five Elements, according to the herb's color, flavor and temperature.

"Unfortunately, there were problems. First of all, it was difficult to verify the taste and temperature of many herbs, because no one could agree on how such qualities could be objectively determined. For example, Jia Yuan Su, a Song Dynasty physician, concluded that the temperature of croton seeds was weak-hot and that the flavor was weak-bitter. His pupil, Li Kao, on the other hand, concluded the temperature was hot and the flavor was acrid.[70] Secondly, in some cases, the theoretical results did not agree with the empirically observed effects.[71] That is, certain herbs did not demonstrate therapeutic properties expected on the basis of their color, flavor and temperature. So if you are a Western doctor and your empirical data doesn't agree with your theoretical expectations, what do you do?"

"Well, assuming that the data is correct, I would search for a new theory to account for the discrepancy."

"Exactly. According to the Western way of thinking, the data is the standard by which you modify the theory. But that's not the method the ancient Chinese doctors used."

"What did they do?"

The room grew silent as Dr. Chang reached for a cup of tea. He took a sip, smiled, then quietly confided, "They worked in reverse."

He continued, "Say you're an ancient traditional Chinese doctor. A patient presents to you with a history and clinical findings consistent with Depletion in the Heart. Now, the Liver is the "Mother" of the Heart, and according to what is known as the "Mother-Child" relationship, when the Child is depleted, the Mother must be replenished.[72] Therefore, in order to replenish the Heart, you must replenish the Liver. According to the Theory of Five Elements, Liver corresponds with sour.[73] Therefore, it follows that the herbs that you use to replenish the Liver must taste sour. The question is, amongst the vast pharmacopoeia of medicinal herbs, which ones taste sour. That's the question."

"Right."

"So, as we were saying before, the Chinese doctors couldn't agree on which herbs tasted sour, but they did know which herbs treated the disease. They knew based on generations of practical experience, as recorded in the pharmaceutical literature. If this herb treats the disease, they reasoned, then it must replenish the Liver. And if the herb replenishes the Liver, then it must taste sour. Therefore, they deduced the taste of the herb based on its known therapeutic activity, rather than determining the taste directly.[74, 75] So a Chinese doctor might tell a patient that this herb treats the disease because it tastes sour, where in truth, the fact that the herb is considered 'sour' was originally deduced from the known actions of the herb. At no point in time was it possible to take an unknown substance, objectively determine its flavor, color and temperature, and based on this information, determine its therapeutic effects.[76]

"In fact, in order to explain the multiple therapeutic effects of some herbs, the Yuan Dynasty physician Chu Chen Heng (1281-1358) argued that herbs could simultaneously taste pungent, sour and sweet.[77] However, if you taste the herbs, many have no distinct "flavor,"[78] and some have no taste at all.[79]

"So, by working in reverse, the facts were made to fit the theory. Whereas Western doctors allow new data to contradict the established model, requiring a new model to be formed, Chinese doctors re-categorize the new data to make the old model work.

"In that manner, the old model never changes. The founding principles stay the same. The data is re-categorized.

The categories are rearranged. Understand that, and you can begin to understand Chinese medicine."

## -- 8 --
## Chinese Pharmacopoeia;
## The Number of Chinese Herbs

I was visiting Thomas the next evening when I noticed a jar of Chinese herbs on the table. I picked them up to take a closer look. The herbs were indicated for various illnesses, but the name on the jar had worn off. I began to wonder what the herbs might be called.

In English, the tendency seems to be toward long and complicated drug names. There is "ibuprofen," "acetaminophen" and "diltiazem." The names are difficult to remember and difficult to spell. In Chinese, however, the names of herbs are like other names in Chinese--they are simple combinations of Chinese characters.

Then I thought to myself, if a name in Chinese is a brief description of an object, like the term "vertical-rise-machine" for the English word "helicopter," then you need to know something about the object before you can give it a name. For example, you would have to categorize an object as a "ji" (machine) or a "che" (vehicle) before you decide to call it one or the other. Similarly, if an herb's name tells you what the herb is used for, you would need to know something about the herb's function before you name it. But what if the function was later shown to be different? Would you give the herb a new name, or would you keep the old name and just remember the new meaning?"

This seemed like a reasonable question, so early the next morning, I walked over to ask Dr. Chang.

His answer was completely unexpected. "The name of the herb probably has little connection to its ultimate therapeutic use," he replied. "An herb is often named for some physical characteristic or the area from which herb was discovered.[80] Furthermore, no matter what the herb is called, the use of the herb is infinitely more complex than can be conveyed by a few simple terms. But truthfully, naming Chinese herbs is not really a problem. That's because there are no new herbs."

"No new herbs?"

Dr. Chang signaled me to walk to the shelf and pick up a small, worn book. The cover read *Zhong Yao Shou Ce* with an accompanying translation, *Handbook of Traditional Chinese Herbs*. He flipped through the book until he found what he looking for: a graph. The vertical axis read, "Number of Chinese Herbs." On the horizontal axis there were dates.

He started, "The Chinese tradition of 'Ben Cao,' translated 'Materia Medica' or 'Pharmacopoeia,' consists of an epic series of books in which the Chinese gathered their vast knowledge of plant, animal and mineral substances."[81]

Dr. Chang pointed to the beginning of the graph.

"The first Ben Cao supposedly dates from 2700 BC when the legendary emperor Shen Nong, considered the father of herbal medicine, tasted and compiled all known medicinal herbs. The text, the *Shen Nong Ben Cao,*[82] survives in a copy made in the 2nd century AD and contains **365** medicinal substances, one for each day of the year."

He adjusted his glasses, moved his finger to the next point, and then continued.

"This volume was then updated and revised just prior to the Tang Dynasty via the meticulous efforts of Tao Hong Jing who doubled the number of herbs to **730**."[83]

"Then in the mid-7th century, the Tang Dynasty government assembled 22 pharmacologists under Su Jing to compile the *Xin Xiu Ben Cao.*[84] It was China's first illustrated pharmacopoeia, included several foreign herbs, and became the official pharmacopoeia of the Tang Dynasty. It listed **850** medicinal substances."

The graph was rising at a steady pace. Dr. Chang continued, "During the Song Dynasty, the emperor ordered Liu Han to revise the *Xin Xiu Ben Cao*. This work, entitled the *Kai Bao Ben Cao*,[85] was published in 973 AD and contained **983** herbs."

"In 1061 AD, still during the Song Dynasty, Zhang Yu Xi revised the *Kai Bao Ben Cao*.[86] This new work contained **1,084** varieties of herbs."

"Then came Tang Shen Wei, whose book entitled *Zheng Lei Ben Cao*[87] became the major pharmacopoeia of the Song dynasty. It increased the number of herbs to **1,744**.

"Finally," he said, "we come to the Ming dynasty, and the most famous and highly regarded Chinese pharmacopoeia of them all: Li Shi Zhen's *Ben Cao Gang Mu*.[88]

"Li Shi Zhen was born in 1518 just north of the Yangtze River.[89] Although interested in the civil service, he eventually pursued a career in medicine. He was an avid scholar and devoted himself to the pharmaceutical literature. However, he soon discovered numerous inaccuracies. He thus undertook the unprecedented task of writing his own fully revised materia medica. Previously, only teams of physicians under imperial order had attempted such a project. Over a period of 27 years, he carefully categorized and meticulously delineated the origins, properties and preparations of each herb. The 52 volume product was published in 1596, 3 years after Li Shi Zhen's death. Li Shi Zhen's work increased the total number of herbs to **1,892**.

"During the Qing Dynasty, there were several more *Ben Cao* volumes, the most notable of which was Zhao Xue Min's *Ben Cao Gang Mu Shi Yi*.[90] Zhao Xue Min's volume increased the number of herbs to 2,608, but people criticized for him wanting to improve on Li Shi Zhen's work.[91]

"Today, there are almost no new Chinese herbs." He pointed to the place where the graph ended. "Li Shi Zhen's *Ben Cao Gang Mu* with 1,892 herbs remains the definitive Chinese herbal text."[92]

1,892 was certainly a lot of herbs, but I was still perplexed. "Why are there are no new herbs?"

"People can't find any," he replied.

"That doesn't make sense," I responded, "In Western medicine there are new drugs. People can find new herbs. There is always some new leaf or new root."

Then he thought again. "There aren't really any new Chinese herbs," he said finally. "There are only new herb combinations."

I heard that word "combinations" and my heart nearly leaped from my chest. "I just had this conversation! It's just like the Chinese characters."

"Exactly."

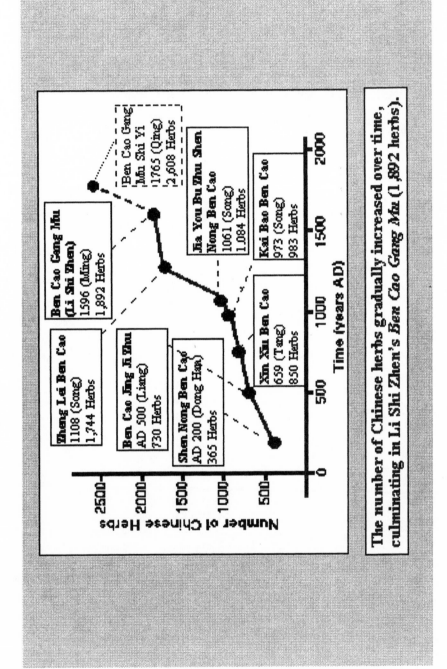

The number of Chinese herbs gradually increased over time, culminating in Li Shi Zhen's *Ben Cao Gang Mu* (1,892 herbs).

## -- 9 --
## Confucian Philosophy and Chinese Herbs; Language, Philosophy and Medicine: An Overview

Now I was frantic. Returning to the dormitory, I paced up and down the hallway, flipping through Dr. Chang's small black book. Although there were a total of 1,892 herbs, only some 230 were in common use. Herbs could be used alone, but they were more often prescribed in combinations. Of course, these combinations were not random assortments of varying substances. Rather, like steaming bowls of savory stir-fry, they were carefully conceived arrangements in which each herb performed a specific role.

In fact, the role and title of each herb was directly adopted from the pre-Confucian, Zhou Dynasty feudal hierarchy. For example, within each combination, there were the Chief, the Deputies, the Assistants and the Envoys. The Chief (*Jun*) was most important and provided the main therapeutic thrust. Deputies (*Chen*) were supportive and enhanced the effects of the Chief. The Assistants (*Zuo*) treated the symptoms and countered the toxicity of the Chief and Deputies. The Envoy (*Shi*) directed the focus of the attack.[93]

Consider, for example, "Ma Huang Tang" or "Yellow Herb Soup," a popular Qing Dynasty remedy for colds.[94] The Chief is *Ma Huang* (Herba Ephedrae), a warm and acrid herb, which directly attacks the cold-induced disorder. The First Deputy, 'cinnamon,'[95] assists the actions of the Chief and facilitates the flow of *Qi* in the channels. The Second Deputy, 'apricot,'[96] assists the Chief with the wheezing. Finally, the Assistant, 'licorice,'[97] moderates the actions of the both the Chief and the Deputies and produces greater harmony overall.[98]

Of course, in addition to this "hierarchical" type of herbal remedy, there are other types of herbal combinations as well. These combinations were traditionally described in the *Shen Nong Ben Cao*, and further developed in the *Ben Cao Gang Mu*.[99]

"Single Effect" (*dan xing*) remedies are the least common type in which one herb is used in isolation. In "Mutual Accentuation" (*xiang xu*), there are two similar herbs, which work to enhance the overall effect. In "Mutual Antagonism" (*xiang wu*), two herbs are opposed, in order to minimize the other's effects. There is "Mutual Counteraction" (*xiang wei*), "Mutual Enhancement" (*xiang shi*) and "Mutual Incompatibility" (*xiang fan*), as well. Each type of combination represents a different type of "relationship" that exists among the herbs in the remedy.

Furthermore, any one herb can play more than one role, depending on the particular combination. In one combination the herb is "supportive." In the next combination the herb is "opposed." The function of the herb depends on the composition of its herbal environment.

In fact, the guidelines for combining Chinese herbs, with the various "Hierarchical," "Synonym," and "Antonym" compounds, were almost identical to the guidelines for combining Chinese characters. Dr. Chang's herbal handbook read like Yuen Ren Chao's *Grammar of Spoken Chinese*.

I stopped to review what I had learned. A limited number of Chinese characters were combined and recombined to make an infinite number of character combinations. Each individual character, written as a distinct and isolated unit, articulated by a single, isolated monosyllable, had its own individual meaning. The combination of characters, however, taken as a whole, had a meaning separate and usually more specific than the meaning of the parts.

In almost identical fashion, a fixed vocabulary of Chinese herbs could be combined to make an infinite number of herbal combinations. Within any combination of characters or herbs, there was a specific relationship among the individual parts. Furthermore, the increase and plateau of characters in dictionaries paralleled the increase and plateau of herbs in pharmacopoeias. Finally, both herbs and characters were treated as whole units. They were intrinsically complex, but irreducible wholes.

Any new vocabulary was a combination of Chinese characters. Any new remedy was a combination of Chinese herbs. In Chinese medicine, any new data was interpreted in terms of a fixed set of irreducible philosophical categories. Could all of this be a coincidence?

Chinese history, philosophy, medicine and cooking were the historical products of the Chinese mind. It seemed intuitively possible that the Chinese language had influenced the development of Chinese thought.

I teetered back and forth. I was walking on dangerous ground. The connection between language and thought was one of the world's most profound and perplexing philosophical questions. The idea that English and Chinese, because of some inherent structural difference, could have influenced the development of two systems of thought was in exact opposition to modern linguistic teaching. Modern linguistics teaches Universal Grammar. In Universal Grammar there is one system of thought. "We all have the same minds,"[7] explains linguist Steven Pinker. Differences among languages are superficial and unimportant.

But it just wasn't right. Whether it was history, philosophy, medicine or cooking, the same patterns of thought emerged again and again. Between China and the West there were two distinct systems of thought, and everything seemed to follow from the organization of the characters.

But how could Chinese characters have such a profound effect? What could be the possible mechanism? Any one character can take on a range of possible meanings. The meanings are not restricted in any particular way. And yet, it is not even the specific characters that seem to matter. It's the organization of the characters overall. Why should the organization of thought follow from the organization of characters?

If the Chinese language did somehow influence the structure of Chinese thought, I decided, then it was probably not the result of the written characters. Rather, it was a result of the spoken sounds. Children learn to speak long before they can read or write. In the history of society spoken language developed first. Clearly, no society developed a written language without first developing a spoken one.

But what was it about spoken Chinese that could influence the structure Chinese thought? Was it the tones? Was it the pronunciation? I lay on the bed and pondered.

## -- 10 --
## A Child's Perspective:
## The Relation between Sound and Symbol

For a young child, language acquisition is one of the most natural and effortless activities. Consider the sequence of events.[100] A baby hits the cold air, gets a glimpse of the world, and the first thing he does is cry. Crying turns to cooing. Cooing turns to babbling. Then, at twelve months of age, the child speaks with one-word sentences. Soon, one-word sentences progress to two-word sentences. These two-word sentences are often described as "telegraphic," resembling the non-inflecting, staccato language of telegrams. Finally, after another length of time, the child's words start to inflect. "Car" becomes "cars" when it changes in number. The verb "watch" becomes "watched" when it changes in tense. By the age of five years, even if not grammatically perfect, the child's speech fully inflects.

Of course, learning to write is an entirely different story. That is just one long, tedious task. Several months had passed since my first Chinese lesson. I could read and write maybe 200-300 characters. But even though I knew more characters than a five-year-old, a five-year old could speak with many more words. Children knew words for everything. I would have felt lucky to speak with the vocabulary of a five-year old.

It then occurred to me that in learning Chinese, there is a fundamental difference between a student and a child. Take my case, for example. I studied Chinese in the university. Each day during class Professor Wei presented 5-10 new characters, including grammatical notes and character combinations. We began with simple, commonly used characters, and then progressed to more difficult ones. Each character had a specific number of strokes, as well as a meaning and a pronunciation.

We learned that there are approximately 400 syllables in Mandarin Chinese,[101,102] spoken with one of 4 possible tones. To the Western ear, the syllables sound remarkably alike, so we were taught "pin-yin" or "romanization." Each syllable was analyzed into three separate parts: an "initial," a "middle" and a "final." The syllable "huang" meaning "yellow," for example, could be broken into "he," "u" and "ang." We were taught that only certain sounds could appear in certain places, which allowed for only a limited number of spoken syllables.

The tone was also important. The same spoken syllable with one of four different tones could take a range of completely different meanings. There was the "level" tone, the "rising" tone, the "dipping" tone and the "falling" tone. The syllable "ma," for example, could be pronounced in four different ways. Each pronunciation had a different meaning: "mother," "hemp," "horse" and "scold."

So every day after class, I returned to my room and practiced my characters. I memorized the meaning, and I memorized the pronunciation. After several attempts at writing each one, I finally remembered the strokes. But I would always forget. First I would forget the strokes. Then I would forget the tone. Finally, like an old acquaintance, I would recall having seen the character, but not remember when or where. So studying Chinese as a foreigner, it is possible to see a character, remember the meaning, but forget the pronunciation--or likewise see a character, remember the pronunciation, but totally forget the meaning.

For a child, however, this situation would be completely absurd. You could never remember the pronunciation and forget the meaning. That's because the native speaker, even if he or she doesn't know the written characters, is already fluent in spoken Chinese. A child knows sounds and their meanings. The two would be completely inseparable. Reading for a child would be a matter of recognizing the spoken sounds in their written form.

The connection between language and thought, I decided, lay somewhere in the difference between spoken and written Chinese. Perhaps I was thinking too much about the Chinese language as written characters with spoken pronunciations. I needed to consider the Chinese language as spoken syllables with written representations.

Consider the following: A foreign student of Chinese learns written characters one by one. Each character has a pronunciation, and each character has a meaning. Of course, a single character can have more than one meaning, and different characters can have the same pronunciation. Characters with the same pronunciation can be compared to "homophones" in English, such as "to," "two" and "too." A Chinese dictionary, for example, lists over twenty different characters with the same pronunciation "yi."

A child, on the other hand, cannot read or write. His language consists only of sounds. The question is, when the child says a particular syllable, does he know what character he is saying? For example, three different combinations use the same syllable "gong": *gong che* ("public-vehicle" or "bus"), *gong ji* ("male-chicken" or "rooster"), and *gong zuo* ("work-work" or simply "work"). The first *gong* means "public," the second *gong* means "male," and the third *gong* means "work." The first two *gong*'s are written with the same Chinese character, 公. The third *gong* is written as 工. All three meanings are different. Two are written the same. Does a child know which meanings go with which characters?

I walked back to ask my instructor, Professor Wei. Her answer was succinct.

"Well," she replied, "A child might recognize a change in meaning when 'gong' is used in different ways. But he doesn't know which character would be used to write which meaning. He only knows the sounds."

And that was the key. As a student of Chinese, you eventually realize that there are only a limited number of spoken monosyllables. Every new character you learn has the same pronunciation as some other character you already know. There is "bo," "bao" and "ban" as well as "xi," "ji" and "qi." You can list the syllables all on a page. In Mandarin Chinese, the number of syllables is approximately 400. That's it. Add to that, one of four possible tones, and you have a total of 1600 possible monosyllable pronunciations. However, not all pronunciations are used, so the total number of syllables is more like 1200. And 1200 syllables are precisely what a child would know.[103]

But the Chinese language has the additional feature that every spoken syllable has it own separate meaning. This meaning is apparent to the native speaker, whether or not he knows the corresponding characters.

Consider the English word "helicopter." The word is written as a continuous sequence of letters, articulated by a more or less uninterrupted unit of sound. You can break the word into four syllables, "hel-i-cop-ter," like you might find in a dictionary, but to the average speaker of English, it is not easy to say where one syllable ends and the next syllable begins. One might just as easily break the "heli" portion into "he-li" instead of "hel-i." In English, all the sounds blend together. Furthermore, even if a person knows Greek and Latin roots, it is not often clear what the meanings of the individual syllables are, even if separate meanings can be said to exist.

In Chinese, however, there is a very clear demarcation from one syllable to the next. The Chinese combination *zhi-sheng-ji* ("vertical-rise-machine") meaning "helicopter," for example, is enunciated as three separate units: *zhi*, *sheng* and *ji*. Unlike English, the sounds are not blended together. As linguist Geoffrey Sampson explains,

> Chinese is a language in which syllables are clearly demarcated from one another phonologically. In English it is normally straightforward to count syllables--river has two, philodendron has four; but it is very difficult to specify where one syllable stops and the next starts--does the /v/ of river end the first syllable or begin the second?...Indeed, questions of the latter category may well be pseudo-questions for a language like English: the truth may well be that the /v/ of river should be treated as belonging to both syllables equally...

> This sort of thinking does not occur in Chinese: in that language, any consonant can easily and unambiguously be identified either as closing one syllable or as opening another, so that the boundaries between syllables are obvious.[105]

Furthermore, even though a child may initially regard *zhi-sheng-ji* as one meaningful unit, he will eventually become aware of the meaning of the parts. That is because a syllable combination is usually just a simple description of the object itself. Not only is there a *zhi-sheng-ji*, but there are other types of *-ji*, as well. There is a *zhao-xiang-ji*

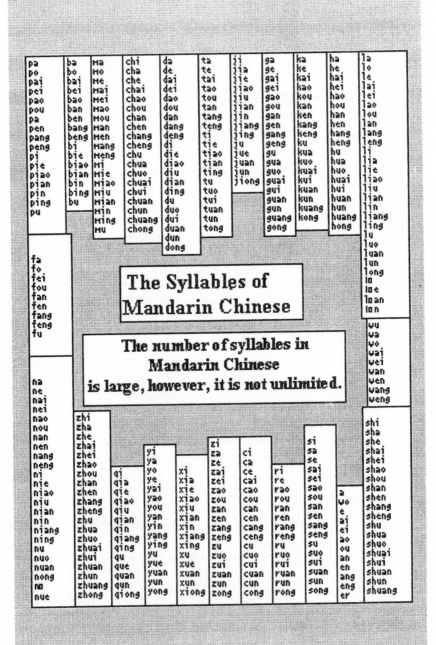

The Syllables of Mandarin Chinese

The number of syllables in Mandarin Chinese is large, however, it is not unlimited.

("take-picture-machine" or camera) and a *dian-shi-ji* ("electric-watch-machine" or television). Any new machine will be some new type of "-ji." Furthermore, the other syllables, *zhi* and *sheng*, also appear in a variety of combinations. Therefore, the average speaker of Chinese, even with no knowledge of Chinese characters, knows both the meaning of the syllables and the meaning of the combinations.

I reviewed what I had learned. A limited number of spoken syllables, continually recombined, was the framework for the written characters, also recombined. The comparisons between medicine, cooking, herbs and characters now could be extended to the spoken syllable.

But something still wasn't right. Why were there only 400 spoken syllables in Mandarin Chinese? Why weren't there any new ones? After all, English seemed to have new syllables. Something about the Chinese language prevented its speakers from creating new syllables.

A television program was featuring a Chinese acrobatic act. It was interesting to watch. The acrobats would take something simple, like a rice bowl. One person would flip it on his head, roll it down his shoulders, and do cartwheels with it. They performed a dozen variations on the same simple theme.

"The many have one essence, and the one has many manifestations," said Thomas. "There are innumerable differences among things in the world, and yet everything originates from one source."[105] My mind was obscured by the myriad of manifestations. It was time that I go to the source. Hidden deep beneath the surface of that syllabic sound, lay the cryptic connection between language and thought.

## -- 11 --
## The Monastery; A Moment of Solitude; The Connection between Language and Thought

Night had fallen. The monks had prepared a delicious meal of vegetable stir-fry and were now in evening prayer.

There was one more question to answer. From a Western perspective, it seemed curious that the Chinese herbs were never reduced into more simple components. Given a medicinal substance, it seems almost intuitive that you would want to break it apart and isolate the active ingredient.[106] But from the Chinese perspective, whether the herb was a leaf or a root, it was always the whole leaf or the whole root.

I remembered a conversation I once had with Dr. Chang.

"That's because for the Chinese, herbs are indivisible units," he said. "If you break them apart, you lose the function of the whole."

"But why? The active ingredient should continue to work."

He thought for a moment. "It's the Chinese philosophy. Take, for example, this stone." He reached for a small green jade, hanging from a cord around his neck. He held the stone in his hand and then gently squeezed it. "It was my mother's stone, given to her on her 1st birthday. Since her death, I wear it always. It brings me good luck.

"Because you are curious," he continued, "you ask me how this stone works. I tell you that it's a lucky stone. It works by luck."

"Of course, as a Westerner, you're not satisfied with that answer. If the stone works at all, there must be some good underlying scientific explanation."

"I give the stone to you, and you take the stone to the laboratory. You break it into a dozen separate pieces. You do experiments to determine which component gives the stone its lucky properties."

"But you see, you missed the point. A lucky stone works as a whole. You can't break it into pieces. If you break the stone into pieces, it no longer works."

I don't know if it was the glow of the lamps or something in that herbal tea, but the evening air had become much more warm and comfortable. I decided to take a walk along the grounds. Just the shadowy glow of lanterns and the fragrant smell of stir-fry filled the air. The wind blew soft and silent.

My thoughts gradually drifted toward the enigmatic Chinese character. Characters represented spoken syllables which were limited in number and continually recombined. That we already knew. Philosophy, cooking, history and medicine--the entire spectrum of Chinese thought followed from the pattern of syllables.

But why was there only a limited set of syllables? Why should there only be 400? English seemed to have new syllables. For example, it's always possible to create a new combination of letters. But Chinese had no new syllables. Mandarin had "pan" and "huan" but no "puan." Why should "p-u-a-n" be so difficult?

Exiting the grounds, I entered a path along the cliff. Against the starlit sky, the moon, like a giant disk of antique jade, was beginning its ascent over the distant horizon. The light reflected gently off a layer of frost in the path. It was a funny thing that moon. No matter where you were, or what era you lived in, you looked up and you saw the same moon. The woods were dark and sullen. There was a quiet rush of wind and an occasional gurgle of water. The air was perfectly clear.

Turning back, I rounded the bend and headed directly for the monastery. Climbing the path, I pressed forward, ready to enter the grounds--when suddenly, without warning, I stopped. I could only gaze in awe. There, straight ahead, beyond two lone pines delicately balanced on the edge of the cliff, an enormous panorama, miles across, unrolled its scene like a giant scroll before my eyes. I had never seen landscape in this way before. Mountains ascended the horizon, raising jagged peaks and wooded slopes. A magnificent stream tumbled downward, burying rocks and shrubs and trees. And at the foot of the monastery, mid-distance, just where the moon had cast the first rays of the evening, an old man, the only sign of human existence, sat in quiet contemplation. It was like a scene from a Ming Dynasty poem:

> White clouds, like a belt, wind around the waist of the mountains;
> A path narrow and long soars into the void, off a stony ledge.
> Alone, I lean on a thornwood staff and gaze peacefully into the distance;
> Wishing to respond with my flute playing to the singing of the mountain stream.[107]

Everything pulsed with rhythm and energy, everything flowed with movement and life. Mutually consuming and mutually increasing--each separate element was changing in meaning, yet was steadfastly constant in structure and sound--and then it struck me: the difference between English and Chinese. It was in the syllables. English syllables were composites of sound. Chinese syllables were not.

Consider the child again. The English-speaking child, even before he or she learns the letters of the alphabet, knows that syllables can be broken apart and rearranged. That's because English syllables are not fixed. "Car" becomes "cars" when it changes in number. "Watch" becomes "watched" when it changes in tense. This change in sound with a change in meaning is what linguists call "inflection." Furthermore, the English-speaking child has an ever-increasing vocabulary of new words. New words contain new syllables and new combinations of sound.

The Chinese child, on the other hand, knows only 400 syllables. He or she learns them separately, one at a time. After 400 syllables, over the course of a lifetime, there are no new syllables. All grammar is expressed as combinations. All new vocabulary consists of whole-number rearrangements of the same fixed, limited set. Within combinations, each syllable remains a separate, isolated unit. Which is to say, a native Chinese speaker never recombines sound to make new syllables, and as for breaking apart old syllables, never learns how.

The ability to break apart syllables is not an inherent ability. It's an ability that is *learned*. After all, when the Chinese learn "pin-yin" or "romanization" as children, they learn to break apart the syllables in order to represent them by the Latin alphabet. The Chinese word "pin-yin" literally means "combine sounds."

Furthermore, even though Chinese syllables *can* be broken into separate sounds, those sounds, and the letters that represent them, are not productive in any way. For example, there is never a need to "spell out" the pronunciation of a character in Chinese. When a Chinese person learns the pronunciation of a character to which he is not familiar, it is explained by referring to the pronunciation of a character which the person already knows.

Thomas was right. The principle of the problem was in my own mind. The English alphabet, with its more precise representation of sound, had fooled me into breaking apart the Chinese syllable. I had assumed that because English syllables could be broken into sounds, Chinese syllables could be broken into sounds as well--as if the Chinese syllable "huang" could be divided into three constituent parts: "he," "u" and "ang." In fact, the written word "huang" is a Western invention,[108] created by the speakers of an inflecting language. In Chinese, the word is written 黃. The character represents the whole syllable.

I then realized that the traditionally accepted sequence of language acquisition--from telegraphic speech, to speech that inflects--does not apply in the Chinese case, simply because the Chinese language does not inflect. English-speaking children move from telegraphic words to word inflections. Chinese-speaking children move from telegraphic words to word combinations. The individual's psychology of language develops at the earliest of formative years.

In fact, not only are there no inflections in Chinese, there are no "rules" required to create them. The desire to break down words into regular rules is strictly a Western phenomenon.

The entire problem of Chinese language and thought began to crystallize in my mind. It wasn't the meaning or configuration of individual words that mattered. It wasn't even the grammar. It was the organization of sound within the language. The manner in which the Chinese mind had learned to organize fixed units of meaningful sound into meaningful combinations had guided the organization of the other entities as well: ingredients into recipes, herbs into remedies, events into history and people into society.

Furthermore, the spoken Chinese syllable as a fixed and irreducible unit could now be extended to other aspects of Chinese culture: herbs as whole substances, dynasties as homogenous units and philosophical categories as irreducible wholes. Which interestingly, directly contrasted with the Western approach--where syllables contained sounds, herbs contained chemicals, history was meticulously analyzed and philosophical categories could be reduced to their most fundamental components.

Finally, the intense interest with which the Chinese examine roles and relationships within a group is a direct reflection of the language, in which syllables all play different roles within the combination. Depending on their relation to other syllables, syllables change in meaning. Likewise, it's a concept of *Qi* that changes in function with its varying roles in the human body, and an ancient society that transforms itself with the changing needs of the situation.

Language and thought are not independent. Rather, they are intimately connected. The nature of our particular language profoundly influences the way that we think. The mind that created Chinese medicine, created Chinese history, philosophy and cooking as well. It wasn't just a coincidence. It was the mind that thought in Chinese.

Poem and calligraphy on previous page from Shen Chou (1427-1509)
*Poet on a Mountain Top*
Courtesy of the Collection of the Nelson-Atkins Museum of Art
Kansas City, Missouri
(Purchase: Nelson Trust) 46-51/2

## Conclusion

Linguistics is the study of language. Or rather, the *scientific* study of language, as most textbooks would have it stated. Language, of course, is familiar to us all. It permeates every aspect of our lives--from our innermost thoughts, to our interaction with others, to our relation to culture as a whole. It begins from the time we are the youngest of children, and persists, if you will, to our last dying word. *Linguistics*, on the other hand, is something different. It investigates the topics pertaining to language--the rhythms of speech, the etymology of words, the structures of grammar, and, of course, the relationship between language and thought.

The question of the relationship between "language and thought" arouses such passion and interest because it is pertinent to the way that we understand ourselves. Clearly, we all "think," and most people will accept that "thought" is a sort of inner dialogue.[109] Furthermore, at least on a superficial level, there appears to be tremendous diversity in terms of vocabulary, grammar and sound structure among the various world languages. The question is, "Does the nature of our particular language influence the way that we think?"

Historically, in linguistics, there have been two camps: Those that believe that language influences thought, and those that believe that thought is independent of language. The first camp is represented in its most extreme view by what is now termed the "Sapir-Whorf hypothesis." The second camp is represented by the theory of "Universal Grammar" as described by linguist Noam Chomsky.

Benjamin Lee Whorf (1897-1941) was an inspector for the Hartford Fire Insurance Company in Hartford, Connecticut, whose interest in Native American languages prompted him to take courses from respected Yale linguist and anthropologist, Edward Sapir. It was during his study of the Hopi Indians that Whorf decided that the Hopi concept of "time" was fundamentally different from the Western concept of "time." He wrote,

> I find it gratuitous to assume that a Hopi who knows only the
> Hopi language and the cultural ideas of his own society has the
> same ideas ... of time and space that we have ... In particular,
> he has no general notion or intuition of TIME as a smooth

flowing continuum in which everything in the universe proceeds as an equal rate.[110]

Whorf believed that this different conception of time was reflected in the grammar of the Hopi language:

> After a long and careful study and analysis, the Hopi language is seen to contain no words, grammatical forms, constructions or expressions that refer directly to what we call "time."[111]

It was this observation as well as many others that prompted Whorf to make his famous statement regarding the relationship between language and thought:

> We dissect nature along lines laid down by our native languages. The categories and types that we isolate from the world of phenomena we do not find there because they stare every observer in the face; on the contrary, the world is presented in a kaleidoscopic flux of impressions which has to be organized by our minds--and this means largely by the linguistic systems in our minds. We cut nature up, organize it into concepts, and ascribe significances as we do, largely because we are parties to an agreement to organize it in this way--an agreement that holds throughout our speech community and is codified in the patterns of our language. The agreement is, of course, an implicit and unstated one, *but its terms are absolutely obligatory*; we cannot talk at all except by subscribing to the organization and classification of data which the agreement decrees.[112]

Hence, according to Whorf, language influences thought. The language which a person speaks influences the manner in which he thinks. Whorf writes,

> A person's thoughts are controlled by inexorable laws of
> pattern of which he is unconscious. These patterns are the
> unperceived intricate systematizations of his own language--
> shown readily enough by a candid comparison and contrast
> with other languages...thinking itself is in a language--in
> English, in Sanskrit, in Chinese.[113]

Whorf died at the young age of forty-four. His papers were
published in 1956, fourteen years after his death. It was at that time that
linguists formulated the two tenets of the Sapir-Whorf hypothesis:

1)  Linguistic relativity: There is no limit to the structural diversity
    of languages
2)  Linguistic determinism: Language determines thought

Of course, not everyone agreed with Whorf's interpretation of the
Hopi concept of time, or for that matter, his interpretation of the Hopi
language. Although widely debated, his ideas were sparsely accepted.
First of all, it was difficult for people to accept that language could have
such a profound influence on thought. For example, whether we decide
to call something a "tree" like we do in English, or a "shu" like they do
in Chinese, our perception of that object is more or less the same. Our
knowledge of that object is infinitely more complex than can be
conveyed by one simple term. The name itself is arbitrary.
Secondly, Whorf's arguments were circular. There was no way

to independently describe the Hopi concept of "time." Any description of "time" was ultimately based on the Hopi language.

Then came Noam Chomsky. It was almost identical to the time that Whorf's theories were being discussed that Chomsky published his book, *Syntactic Structures*. It was a book whose ideas were so influential, it created the so-called "Chomskyan Revolution."

Until Chomsky, linguistics was mostly descriptive. It sought to classify the various world languages, organize and simplify the complex sounds of speech, and provide a detailed "grammar" of each of the world's languages. Linguists provided complete descriptions of the different parts of speech, and how they interact to form meaning within a sentence. From there, linguists sought to describe how languages change over time, and how they adapt to new circumstances.

A linguist at MIT, Chomsky was impressed with the ease with which young children acquire language. As Chomsky noted, any given language contains an infinite number of possible sentences. Some sentences are grammatical, and some sentences are not. With little formal instruction, children are able to produce both original and grammatical combinations of words. They rarely speak ungrammatically. Chomsky concluded that there must be a set of "rules," part of the inherited structure of the human brain, that guides the acquisition of language. Because all humans possess language ability, and any child can learn any language, these rules were believed to be "universal." That is, despite the seeming complexity of the various world languages, there is a single mental design or "universal grammar" that underlies them all.

Chomsky explains,

> In a given linguistic community, children with very different experience arrive at comparable grammars...Each child is confronted with different data—but in the end the system is essentially the same. As a consequence we have to suppose that all children share the same internal constraints which characterize narrowly the grammar they are going to construct.[114]

He also writes,

> Although [traditional] grammars may contain full and explicit lists of exceptions and irregularities, they provide only examples and hints concerning the regular and productive syntactic processes...by a generative grammar I mean simply a system of rules that in some explicit and well-defined way assigns structural descriptions to sentences.[115]

Chomsky's ideas were revolutionary. The notion of an innate language faculty directly contrasted the widely held "Empiricist School" view that language was acquired only through experience.[116] "Universal Grammar" became the dominant theory of modern linguistics. As a result, over the past half-century, the major trend in Western linguistics has been toward the investigation of the Universal Grammar.

The rules of Universal Grammar can be understood, according to Chomsky, but only through the rigorous techniques of scientific analysis. Linguistics, according to Chomsky, is a science, a field in which problems can be reduced to their most fundamental components, models can be constructed and theories can be tested--ultimately revealing the underlying principles or rules. As Chomsky explains, the structure of language can be unraveled in much the same manner that scientists understand problems in biology or physics:

> I think that we should study the problem of language and the mind in the way we study any problem in biology. We can take as an example the ways in which we study the characteristics of organs or systems of the body...
>
> If we were to study the human visual system, we would first attempt to abstract this system away from its physical context...Having done this, the scientist then attempts to discover the structural principles that determine how the system functions...I think that we should study language in exactly the manner of the physical sciences.[117]

Languages, for Chomsky, are more similar than different. They can all be reduced to the same set of rules. In the words of MIT linguist Steven Pinker:

> Universal Grammar is like an archetypal body plan found across vast numbers of animals in a phylum...For example,

among all the amphibians, reptiles, birds, and mammals, there is a common body architecture, with a segmented backbone, four jointed limbs, a tail, a skull, and so on. The various parts can be grotesquely distorted or stunted across animals: a bat's wing is a hand, a horse trots on its middle toes, whales' forelimbs have become flippers...Many of these differences are caused by minor variations in the relative timing and rate of growth of the parts of embryonic development.

Differences among languages are similar. There seems to be a common plan of syntactic, morphologic, and phonological rules and principles, with a small set of varying parameters, like a checklist of options. Once set, a parameter can have far-reaching changes on the superficial appearance of the language.[118]

What is the relationship between language and thought in Chomsky's formulation? "Thoughts," whether they are of cooking, philosophy, medicine or language, exist independent of the words used to express them.[119] "Thoughts" begin deep in the mind, guided by the genetically inherited Universal Grammar. Words are the outer label of thoughts. They are the arbitrary result of a person's specific language upbringing. Chomsky explains,

Try to define a word like 'table' or book or whatever, and you'll find it's extremely difficult...A recent issue of a linguistics journal...has a long detailed article trying to give the meaning of the word 'climb.' And it is very complicated, but every child learns it perfectly right away...Now this can mean only one thing. Namely, human nature (innate ideas) give us the concept 'climb' for free...

This is the way we learn language. We simple learn the label that goes with the preexisting concept. So in other words, it is as if the child, prior to any experience, has a long list of concepts like 'climb,' and then the child is looking at the world to figure out which sound goes with which concept.[120]

This separation of language and thought is further emphasized by Pinker, in his emphatic refutation of the Sapir-Whorf hypothesis:

> Supposedly there is a scientific basis for these assumptions: the famous Sapir-Whorf hypothesis of linguistic determinism, stating that people's thoughts are determined by the categories made available in their language, and its weaker version, linguistic relativity, stating that differences among the languages cause differences in the thoughts of their speakers. People who remember little else from their college education can rattle off the factoids: the languages that carve the spectrum into color words at different places, the fundamentally different Hopi concept of time, the dozens of Eskimo words for snow. The implication is heavy: the foundational categories of reality are not "in" the world but are imposed by one's culture...
>
> But it is wrong, all wrong. The idea that thought is the same thing as language is an example of what can be called a conventional absurdity: a statement that goes against all common sense but what everyone believes...The idea that language shapes thinking seemed plausible when scientists were in the dark about how thinking works or even how to study it. Now that cognitive scientists know how to think about thinking, there is less of a temptation to equate it with language just because words are more palpable than thoughts...[121]

According to Pinker, language and thought are independent. Your thoughts are not influenced by the language you speak. He continues,

> People do not think in English or Chinese or Apache; they think in a language of thought. This language of thought

probably looks a bit like all these languages...a universal mentalese.[122]

And that is where we stand in modern linguistics. Whorf is in the background, and Chomsky is at the helm, with the majority of scholars accepting the premise that language is independent of thought.

And perhaps Chomsky is right. There may well be an inherited language faculty. There may be a set of rules, evolved over thousands of years, that allows a child to effortlessly and instinctively learn language.

But in Chomsky's theory of language there is one critical flaw. There is one flaw, that while it does not negate the existence of a Universal Grammar, calls into serious question his interpretation of languages outside of English. It is the idea of "science." It is the idea that the structure of language should be studied "scientifically."

Because "science" itself is only a philosophy. It is one particular way of thinking that breaks down the world into regular rules. And it has its roots in Western languages. Universal Grammar is a theory about "rules," formulated in a language which is founded on "rules." The "scientific approach" to the study of language is inherently a Western phenomenon.

Whorf wrote,

> The ideal of worldwide fraternity and cooperation fails if it does not include ability to adjust intellectually as well as emotionally to our brethren in other countries. The West has attained some emotional understanding of the East...but this has not bridged the intellectual gulf.
>
> We are no nearer to understanding the types of logical thinking which are reflected in truly Eastern forms of scientific thought or analysis of nature. This requires linguistic research into the logics of native languages, and realization that they have equal scientific validity with our own thinking habits.[123]

Whorf may not have convinced future generations of linguists on the native "logic" of different languages, but his instincts were right. Language and thought are not independent. Rather, they are intimately connected. The Chinese language and Chinese culture have their own internal logic. Western linguists, by applying their scientific techniques to languages like Chinese, misinterpreted the native linguistic structures. By underestimating the influence of Western linguistic habits, they overlooked the intimate connection between language and thought.

# An Abbreviated Chronology of China[124,125]

Pre-Imperial China:
Prehistory 5000-1650 BC
  **Xia** Dynasty (legendary) 21$^{st}$ -16$^{th}$ century BC
  **Shang** Dynasty 1650-1027 BC
  **Zhou** Dynasty 1027-256 BC

Early Imperial Empire:
  **Qin** Dynasty 221-207 BC
  Early **Han** Dynasty (Western Han) 206 BC-AD 9
  Xin Dynasty 9-23
  Late **Han** Dynasty (Eastern Han) 25-220
  The Three Kingdoms 221-265

Middle Imperial Empire:
  Northern and Southern Dynasties 265-589
  Sui Dynasty 589-618
  **Tang** Dynasty 618-906
  Five Dynasties 907-960
  **Song** Dynasty: Northern Song 960-1126
        Southern Song 1127-1279

Late Imperial Empire:
  **Yuan** Dynasty 1279-1368
  **Ming** Dynasty 1368-1644
  **Qing** Dynasty 1644-1911

Post-Imperial China:
  Republic of China 1912-1949
  People's Republic of China 1949-present

# References

[1] Miller, George. 1996. *The Science of Words*. New York: The Scientific American Library. pg. 40.

[2] Lyons, John. 1981. *Language and Linguistics*. Cambridge: Cambridge University Press. pg. 239.

[3] Fenollosa, Ernest. (editor, Ezra Pound). 1936. *The Chinese Written Character as a Medium for Poetry*. San Francisco: City Light Books. pg. 21.

[4] Ullman, B.L.. *Ancient Writing and Its Influence*. New York: Cooper Square Publishers, Inc. pg. 7.

[5] Bloom, Alfred. 1981. *The Linguistic Shaping of Thought: A Study in the Impact of Language on Thinking in China & the West*. New Jersey: Laurence Erlbaum Associates.

[6] Bodde, Derek. 1991. *Chinese Thought, Society and Science*. Honolulu: University of Hawaii Press. pg. 96.

[7] Pinker, Steven. 1995. *The Language Instinct*. New York: HarperPerenial. pg. 430.

[8] Geng, Junying and Zhihong Su. 1990. *Practical Traditional Chinese Medicine & Pharmacology: Basic Theories and Principles*. Beijing: New World Press. pgs. 6-23.

[9] Chen, Ping. 1999. *Modern Chinese*. Cambridge: Cambridge University Press. pg. 135.

[10] Yip Po-Ching. 2000. *The Chinese Lexicon; A Comprehensive Survey*. London: Routledge. pg. 19. Please note: There are some differences in dates and numbers of characters when comparing the work of Chen and Yip. These differences are minor, however, and I have not annotated each data point separately.

[11] Western (or Early) Han 206 BC to AD 9; Eastern (or Late) Han AD 25 to AD 220.

[12] Hibbert, Christopher. 1981. *The Emperors of China*. Chicago: Stonehenge Press Inc. pg. 65.

[13] Northern Song AD 960-1126; Southern Song AD 1127-1279

[14] Schirokauer, Conrad. 1991. *A Brief History of Chinese Civilization*. San Diego: Harcourt Brace Jovanovich. pgs. 132-161.

[15] Liu, James T.C.. 1988. *China Turning Inward: Intellectual-Political Changes in the Early Twelfth Centuries*. Cambridge: Harvard University, Council on East Asian Studies. pgs. 1-20.

[16] Although Yip includes the 1914 *Zhong Hua Da Zi Dian* with 48,000 characters in his list of Chinese dictionaries, he then writes, "After that the main concern of the lexicon is reflected in the use of a more or less fixed set of mononyms..."

[17] The gradual increase in the number of Chinese characters culminating in the Qing Dynasty *Kang Xi Dictionary* is used here to illustrate the prolific use of character *combinations* in the creation of new vocabulary. However, this example should not be interpreted to mean that the use of combinations began only *after* the Qing Dynasty. Rather, I suspect that combinations were always an integral part of spoken Chinese. As we will see, the use of combinations in spoken Chinese is intimately related to the fact that there are only a limited number of spoken syllables.

[18] The definition of what constitutes a "word" in Chinese is a source of considerable linguistic debate. In the following discussion, the "word" in English will be considered equivalent to the "character combination" in Chinese.

[19] Inflection can be regular or irregular. The majority of verbs are "regular verbs" and their forms follow regular rules. "Watch" and "talk" are examples. Irregular verbs (such as "buy—*bought*" and "go—*went*") represent "exceptions" to the rules and their forms require memorization. For a discussion on regular and irregular verbs, please see Pinker, Steven. 1999. *Words and Rules*. New York: Perennial. pgs. 13-19.

[20] Karlgren, Bernhard. 1962. *Sound and Symbol in Chinese*. Hong Kong: Hong Kong University Press. pg. 12.

[21] Editors of China Pictoral. 1983. *Chinese Cuisine from the Master Chefs of China*. Boston: Little, Brown. pg. 35.: "The Chinese define four elements that blend creatively in every successful dish: 'color,' 'fragrance,' 'flavor,' and 'shape.'" Other authors also add "texture." See Tropp, Barbara. 1982. *The Modern Art of Chinese Cooking*. New York: William Morrow and Co. pg. 17.

[22] Anderson, E.N. 1988. *Ibid.* pg. 191.

[23] Editors of China Pictoral. 1983. *Ibid.* pg. 65.

[24] These, if you will, are part of the "rules" of Western cooking. Carrying the analogy even further, you might say that the structure of the knife "inflects" with respect to the substrate being cut.

[25] Anderson, E.N. 1988. *The Food of China*. New Haven: Yale University Press. pgs. 183-4.

[26] Thomas's quote is from Chong Xin (782-865), adopted from Chung, Tsai Chih (translator, Brian Bruya). 1998. *Wisdom of the Zen Masters*. New York: Doubleday. pg. 95.

[27] Quote adopted from Da Yi (707-86), from Chung, Tsai Chih (trans. Brian Bruya). 1998. *Ibid*. pg. 63.

[28] Quote adopted from Gui Shan Ling You (Tang Dynasty), from Chung, Tsai Chih (translator Brian Bruya).1998. *Ibid*. pg. 76.

[29] Chao, Yuen Ren. 1968. *A Grammar of Spoken Chinese*. Berkeley: University of California Press. pgs 194-257 and 359-495. See also: Ding Sheng Shu. 1963. *Xian Dai Han Yu Yu Fa Jiang Hua*. Bejing: Shang wu yin shu guan ("Commercial Press"). pgs. 218-228.

[30] "Confucius" is the romanized version of "Kong Fu Zi" or "Master Kong."

[31] American society is based on laws and rules. Chinese society is based on "relationships."

[32] Cheng, Te-k'un. 1980. *The World of the Chinese—A Struggle for Human Unity--*. Hong Kong: The Chinese University Press. pg. 79.

[33] Yang, Martin M.C.. 1969. *Chinese Social Structure*. Taipei: Eurasia Book Co.. pg. 61.

[34] Cheng, Te-k'un. 1980. *Ibid*. pg. 79.

[35] Leong, Y and L Tao. 1915. *Villiage and Town Life in China*. London: George Allen & Unwin Ltd.. pg. 16.

[36] Fung, Yu-Lan (editor, Derk Bodde). 1976. *A Short History of Chinese Philosophy*. New York: The Free Press. pg. 21.

[37] Mah, Adeline Yen. 2001. *Watching the Tree*. NY: Broadway Books. pg. 53.

[38] Leong, Y.K. and L.K. Tao. 1915. *Ibid*. pg. 27.

[39] Mah. 2001. *Ibid*. pgs. 53-4.

[40] King, Ambrose Y.C. (editor, Donald Munro). 1985. "The Individual and Group in Confucianism: A Relational Perspective" in *Individualism and Holism: Studies in Confucian and Taoist Values*. Ann Arbor: University of Michigan Press. pg. 58.

[41] Cai Xi Qin (translator). 1994. *Analects of Confucius*. Beijing: Beijing Foreign Languages Printing House. pgs. 214-5 (XII, 11).

[42] Chung, Tsai Chih (translator Brian Bruya). 1996. *Confucius Speaks*. New York: Doubleday. pgs. 171-3.

[43] Lin, Yu Tang.1938.*The Wisdom of Confucius*.NY:Random House.pgs.205-40.

[44] Chung, Tsai Chih (translator Brian Bruya). 1996. *Ibid*. pgs. 171-173.

[45] Dawson, Miles Menander. 1915. *The Ethics of Confucius*. New York: The Knickerbocker Press. pgs. 156-171.

[46] Wu, John C.H. (editor, Charles Moore). 1967. "Chinese Legal and Political Philosophy" in *The Chinese Mind*. Honolulu: East-West Center Press. pg. 227.

[47] Dawson, Miles Menander. 1915. *Ibid*. pgs. 172-4.

[48] Wu, John C.H.. 1967. *Ibid*. pgs. 213-5.

[49] Yang, Martin M.C.. 1969. *Ibid*. pgs. 94-5.

[50] Leong, Y and L Tao. 1915. *Ibid*. pgs. 3-5.

[51] Leong, Y and L Tao. 1915. *Ibid*. pg. 40.

[52] Geng, Juying and Zhihong Su. 1990. *Ibid*. pgs.. 8-11.

[53] *Xin, or* "pungent," is the flavor of horseradish. It can also be translated as "acrid."

[54] Needham, Joseph. 1954. *Ibid.* vol. 2, ch. 13, pg. 280.

[55] Needham, Joseph. 1954. *Ibid.* vol. 2, ch. 13, pg. 286.

[56] Needham, Joseph (with Wang Ling). 1954. *Science and Civilisation in China.* Cambridge: Cambridge University Press. vol. 2, ch. 13, pg. 232. Note: pin yin for Tsou Yen is "Zou Yan."

[57] Unschuld, Paul. 1985. *Medicine in China.* Berkeley: University of California Press. pg. 81.

[58] The "triple burner" or "san jiao" is a general term for three areas of the body (upper, middle, lower). Unschuld, Paul. 1985. *Ibid.* pg. 81.

[59] Geng, Juying and Zhihong Su. 1990. *Ibid.* pgs. 125-161.

[60] Geng, Juying and Zhihong Su. 1990. *Ibid.* pg. 126.

[61] "Although Qi is fundamentally the same, it puts on 'different hats' in different places assuming different functions. For example, Nutritive Qi exists in the Interior of the body. Its function is to nourish and it is denser than Defensive Qi, which is on the Exterior and protects the body. Derangement of either Defensive or Nutritive Qi will give rise to different clinical manifestations and will require different kinds of treatment. Ultimately, though, they are nothing but two different manifestations of the same Qi energy." Giovanni, Maciocia. 1989. *The Foundations of Chinese Medicine.* Edinburgh: Churchill Livingstone. pgs. 37-8.

[62] Although Western theorists look for rules that are "absolute" and "universal," they allow for the possibility that "exceptions" do exist.

[63] Lloyd, G.E.R. 1970. *Early Greek Science: Thales to Aristotle.* New York: W.W. Norton & Co.. pg. 61.

[64] Andreas Vesalius (1514-1564) was a Belgian physician who developed a detailed model of the human body based on anatomic dissections.

[65] For example, the British physician William Harvey (1578-1657) described the circulation of the blood and the pumping of the heart. This model replaced the earlier model proposed by Galen (AD 130-201) in which the heart, similar to the lungs, functioned in respiration. Rothman, David (ed.). 1995. *Medicine and Western Civilization.* New Brunswick, New Jersey: Rutgers University Press. pg. 68-75.

[66] Bensky, Dan and Andrew Gamble (with Ted Kaptchuk). 1986. *Chinese Herbal Medicine: Materia Medica.* Seattle: Eastland Press. pg. 25.

[67] Unschuld, Paul. 1985. *Ibid.* pgs. 179-80.

[68] Unschuld, Paul. 1985. *Ibid.* pg. 180-6. The Five "Temperatures" or "Thermo-influences" are warm, hot, balanced, cool and cold.

[69] Unschuld, Paul. 1985. *Ibid.* pg. 180.

[70] Unschuld, Paul. 1985. *Ibid.* pg. 187.

[71] Unschuld, Paul. 1985. *Ibid.* pg. 187.

[72] Unschuld, Paul. 1986. *Medicine in China; A History of Pharmaceutics.*

Berkeley: University of California Press. pgs. 111-112.

[73] Unschuld, Paul. 1986. *Ibid.* pg. 112.

[74] Long, Zhixian (editor). 1998. *The Chinese Materia Medica.* Beijing: Academy Press. pg. 8.: "Five flavors are determined by actual tasting and experience of clinical applications. Therefore, [the] five flavors as a theory of drug properties [go] far beyond the concept of tasting sensations but [are] closely linked to [the] affects of drugs. That is the reason why flavors recorded in books on materia medica are sometimes different from actual tasting sensations."

[75] Hou, Jinlun (editor). 1994. *Clinical Handbook of Chinese Materia Medica.* Beijing: China Medico Pharmaceutical Science and Technology Publishing House. pg. 2.: "The taste[s] don't necessarily refer to the real tastes of the drugs. Sometimes they are sorted out according to the drugs' actions..."

[76] Unschuld, Paul. 1986. *Ibid.* pg. 110-13. This example is derived from an example by Wang Hao Ku in the *Tang Ye Ben Cao* (AD 1248) as translated by Unschuld. Although I have changed the specifics of Wang Hao Ku's example, I have remained true to his line of reasoning. Also see the discussion by Unschuld which follows: "A first crucial problem discussed in detail in this section is the standardization of drug qualities. Such standardization was necessary in order to arrange drug effects into an accepted mechanism of effects. Since it was not possible to examine the effects of drugs within the organism itself, one was limited to assigning to given or assumed characteristics of drugs a certain positional value in the system of the yinyang and Five Phases theories relevant to the organism and its functions...The subjectivity of human sensory organs, however, hindered this process; for instance, not all drugs described by an author as being 'sour' were so distinctly characterized by taste that every other author would necessarily follow this assertion."

[77] Unschuld, Paul. 1986. *Ibid.* pg. 187.

[78] Unschuld, Paul. 1986. *Ibid.* pg. 187.

[79] A small number of herbs are recognized as having no flavor (*wu wei*) and are typically categorized as "sweet". Please see Long, Zhixian (editor). 1998. *Ibid.* pg. 8-9.: "Tasteless ... flavors still belong to five flavors ... Tasteless flavor belongs to sweet..."

[80] Bensky, Dan and Andrew Gamble (with Ted Kaptchuk). 1986. *Ibid.* Seattle: Eastland Press. pg. 16.

[81] The names (Chin/Eng) and dates of pharmacopoeias are from Hsu, H, et al. 1986.*Oriental Materia Medica.*Long Beach, CA:Oriental Healing Arts Inst.pg.4.

[82] English translation: *Shen Nong's Classic of Pharmaceutics*

[83] Tao Hong Jing's book was entitled *Ben Cao Jing Ji Zhu* (*Classic of Pharmaceutics, Compiled and Annotated*).

[84] English translation: *Materia Medica, Newly Revised*

[85] English translation: *Kai-Bao Period Materia Medica*

[86] Zhang Yu Xi called his work the *Jia You Bu Zhu Shen Nong Ben Cao* (*Shen Nong Materia Medica, Expanded and Annotated during the Jia-You Period*).

[87] English translation: *Materia Medica, Arranged by Types*
[88] English translation: *Materia Medica, Arranged according to Drug Descriptions and Technical Aspects*
[89] Needham, Joseph (with Wang Ling). 1986. *Science and Civilisation in China.* Cambridge: Cambridge University Press. vol. 6, ch. 38, pgs. 308-321.
[90] English translation: *Supplementary Amplifications of the Ben Cao Gang Mu*
[91] Needham, Joseph (with Wang Ling). 1986. *Ibid.* vol. 6, ch. 38, pg. 326.
[92] Needham, Joseph (with Wang Ling). 1986. *Ibid.* vol. 6, ch. 38, pg. 321.: "Afterwards [following the publication of the *Ben Cao Gang Mu*] nothing was ever quite the same. Nearly all of the work of the seventeenth and eighteenth centuries in pharmaceutical natural history derived from that of Li Shih-Chen [Li Shi Zhen]." Also note, although modern pharmacopoeias may list additional herbal substances, most traditional Chinese physicians continue to prescribe the same limited set of approximately 500: "235 herbs...are most commonly used, 146 are less often prescribed, and 141...are rarely given." Hsu, Hong-Yen and et al. 1986. *Oriental Materia Medica; a concise guide.* Long Beach, CA: Oriental Healing Arts Institute. pg. 4.
[93] Bensky, Dan and Randall Barolet. 1990. *Chinese Herbal Medicine: Formulas & Strategies.* Seattle: Eastland Press. pg. 14.
[94] Bensky, Dan and Randall Barolet. 1990. *Ibid.* pg. 15.
[95] *zhi gui* [96] *xing ren* [97] *zhi gan cao*
[98] In this particular remedy there is no Envoy.
[99] Bensky, Dan and Andrew Gamble(with Ted Kaptchuk).1986. *Ibid.* pgs. 11-12.
[100] Lyons, John. 1981. *Ibid.* pgs. 253-257.
   My note: The fact that children learn "rules" for inflection is demonstrated by the fact that they often apply the rules to situations where they are not appropriate (i.e. children may say "buyed," and not "bought").
[101] DeFrancis, John. 1984. *The Chinese Language: Fact and Fantasy.* Honolulu: University of Hawaii Press. pg. 42. DeFrancis explains that number of "basic syllables" in spoken Mandarin Chinese (excluding tones) has been "variously estimated at 398 to 418, depending on 'what form of speech is taken as the basis, and whether exclamations and the like are included.'"
[102] Chen, Arthur G.T. 1983. *Beginning Chinese.* Hong Kong: Swindon Book Company. pgs. 3-11 to 3-14.
[103] Chao, Yuen Ren. 1968. *Ibid.* pg. 200. Chao places the total number of spoken monosyllables (including tones) in standard Mandarin Chinese at 1277.
[104] Sampson, Geoffrey. 1985. *Writing Systems: A Linguistic Introduction.* London: Hutchinson. Pgs. 145-71.
[105] Quote adopted from Ju Zhi, from Chung, Tsai Chih. (translator, Brian Bruya). 1994. *Zen Speaks.* New York: Doubleday. pg. 102.
[106] Words in English, although phonetically whole, can be divided into different meaningful parts. There is often a "stem" (which carries the meaning of word) combined with one several inflectional affixes. For example, "walks," "walking"

and "walked" all carry the common stem "walk." In psychological terms, the stem of the word might represent the word's "active ingredient."

[107] Shen Chou (1427-1509), inscribed on a painting. (translator, Daniel Bryant) in Liu, Wu-chi and Irving Yucheng Lo (editors). 1975. *Sunflower Splendor; Three Thousand Years of Chinese Poetry*. Bloomington: Indiana University Press. pg. 465. A reproduction of the original painting (with calligraphy) can be found in Chaves, Jonathan (editor). 1986. *The Columbia Book of Later Chinese Poetry*. New York: Columbia Press. A reproduction of Shen Chou's calligraphy, courtesy of the Collection of The Nelson-Atkins Museum of Art, Kansas City, Missouri (Purchase: Nelson Trust) 46-51/2, can be seen on page 113 of this book.

[108] DeFrancis, John. 1984. *Ibid.* pgs. 240-287. As DeFrancis explains, "romanization" was originally introduced to China by Western missionaries, although different systems of transcription eventually developed.

[109] Lyons, John. 1981. *Ibid.* pg. 238.

[110] Whorf, Benjamin Lee. 1956. *Language, Thought and Reality*. Cambridge: The M.I.T. Press. pg. 57.

[111] Whorf, Benjamin Lee. 1956. *Ibid.* pg. 57.

[112] Whorf, Benjamin Lee. 1956. *Ibid.* pgs. 213-4.

[113] Whorf, Benjamin Lee. 1956. *Ibid.* pg. 252.

[114] Chomsky, Noam. 1998. *On Language*. New York: The New York Press. pg. 98.

[115] Chomsky, Noam. 1965. *Aspects of the Theory of Syntax*. Cambridge: MIT press. pgs. 5-8. Here, the term "generative grammar" can be understood to mean "universal grammar."

[116] Steinberg, Danny. 1993. *An Introduction to Psycholinguistics*. New York: Longman Publishing. pg. 135.

[117] Chomsky, Noam (editor, C.P. Otero). 1988. *Language and Politics*. Montreal: Black Rose Books. pgs. 253-4.

[118] Pinker, Steven. 1995. *Ibid.* pgs. 238-9.

[119] Steinberg, Danny. 1993. *Ibid.* pg. 118. In Chomsky's formulation, the syntax of language is primary. Meaning and sound are derived secondarily through rules, and they are not directly related to one another.

[120] Chomsky, Noam. 1988. *Language and Problems of Knowledge*. Cambridge: The MIT Press. pgs. 190-1.

[121] Pinker, Steven. 1995. *Ibid.* pgs. 57-9.

[122] Pinker, Steven. 1995. *Ibid.* pgs. 81-2.

[123] Whorf, Benjamin Lee. 1956. *Ibid.* pg. 21.

[124] Clayre, Alasdair. 1984. *Heart of the Dragon*. Boston: Houghton Mifflin. pgs. xi-xiii.

[125] Cotterell, Arthur. 1988. *China: A Cultural History*. New York: Meridian. pgs. 323-4.

## About the Author

Dr. Jeffrey Brown received his degree from the University of Michigan Medical School. He continued his training in Philadelphia, where he currently lives and works. He is an avid student of language and culture. This is his first book.

Additional copies of *Thinking in Chinese* can be ordered from

your local bookstore or purchased online at

Amazon.com

For questions, comments or information about bulk discounts, please
write the author directly at:
thinkinginchinese@yahoo.com